THORVALDSENS
MUSEUM

COPENHAGEN

1953

THORVALDSENS MUSEUM

is the property of the municipality of Copenhagen. As regards the foundation of the Museum there is an inscription on east wall of the building which says as follows:

IN ROME, IN THE YEAR 1837 THORVALDSEN RESOLVED THAT HIS WORKS, COLLECTIONS AND FORTUNE WERE TO DEVOLVE UPON HIS NATIVE CITY OF COPENHAGEN TO FORM A PERSONAL MUSEUM

BY MEANS OF CONTRIBUTIONS FROM KING FREDERIK VI AND KING CHRISTIAN VIII, FROM THE COPENHAGEN CORPORATION AND FROM CICIZENS OF ALL CLASSES, THE WORK WAS COMPLETED IN THE YEAR 1848

The building was erected and decorated after the designs of the architect M. G. Bindesbøll and under his personal supervision. The work was commenced in 1839. Before the building had been completed a wish made itself felt that besides containing his works and collections it should also be Thorvaldsens's last resting-place. After his consent had been obtained, a sepulchral chamber was built in the centre of the courtyard, decorated by the landscape painter H. C. From, with white lilies on a blue ground. Thorvaldsens' coffin was lowered into this chamber on September 6th 1848. An inscription round the granite edge of the grave reads as follows:

BERTEL THORVALDSEN
B. THE 19TH NOVEMBER 1770, D. THE 24TH MARCH 1844

In Thorvaldsen's lifetime the upper part of the street frontages were finished in unornamented stucco, but two years after Thorvaldsen's death Bindesbøll suggested that they should be decorated with a figure frieze. The ideas embodied in its composition are Bindesbøll's. The latter is also supposed to have given directions for the placing of the figures. The composition and exceution, however, are the work of Jørgen Sonne, under whose direction the frieze was executed during the years 1846-48 and 1850 in a unique colour plaster technique, the pictures being not paintings but masonry work in cement plaster mixed up with colour powder.

On the canal frontage is depicted Thorvaldsen's arrival in Copenhagen i 1838. Facing the Palace Chapel is seen the frigate "Rota", from which Thorvaldsen's works are being speedily unloaded. The final transfer of the works of art to the Museum is shown on the wall facing Christiansborg Palace.

The decorations on the courtyard frontages were executed during the summer and autumn of 1844. The laurel trees, the oaks and the palms are the work of the landscape painter H. C. From, while the frieze showing the chariot-race of the genii is the work of the German sculptor Johann Scholl.

The bronze group over the main entrance – Victory stopping her Quadriga – is a gift from King Christian VIII. It was modelled by H.V. Bissen, who used one of Thorvaldsen's sketches for the figure of the goddess and one of Thorvaldsen's models for the inside left horse (No. 125, p. 29). The sketches for the reliefs on the corner pilasters are the work of H. E. Freund, after whose death they were hewn in sandstone by Johan Scholl. Formerly, part of them were painted.

For the decoration of the ceilings Bindesbøll employed a number of artists and quite young Academy pupils, among whom G. C. Hilker, Chr. Købke, Jørgen Sonne, G. Chr. Freund, Heinrich Hansen, A. P. Madsen, and C. F. Sørensen were the most notable. Bindesbøll was the guiding spirit of the work. Under his supervision his assistants worked more or less independently, and the memory of his ability to direct and inspire them still lives. Bindesbøll's decorative skill is particularly displayed in the patterns of the floor mosaics and the terrazzos – an often overlooked but very important part of the harmonious whole which in the interior of the Museum presents.

On September 17th 1848, the tenth anniversary of Thorvaldsen's return from Italy, the Corporation officially took over Thorvaldsen's art collections, and the following day the Museum was opened to the public.

*

As mentioned already, the Museum contains Thorvaldsen's own works as well as his collections. The former comprise a number of drawings (which are not displayed), a large number of plaster sketches, the majority of his original models, various cats, several of his works in marble executed under his own supervision and completed by himself, as well as marble copies made by various artists after the master's death

Thorvaldsen's collections are very comprehensive and furnish the best possible evidence of his wide artistic culture and the versatility of his mind. There are works from ancient Egypt, antique and oriental bronzes; there are gems and coins, especially Greek, in rich profusion; there are also Greek and Roman marbles, a handsome collection of antique

vases and various terra-cotta objects of art. The most outstanding part of the collection, however, consists of paintings.
It contains a few specimens of Renaissance art, but its chief
interest is the remarkable insight it gives into the work of
the painters contemporary with Thorvaldsen. His collections
of watercolours, drawings, engravings, books, and casts
based on antique sculptures, are also important.

BIOGRAPHY OF THORVALDSEN

There is some uncertainty regarding the date of Thorvaldsen's birth. He and his contemporaries thought that he had been born in Grønnegade, Copenhagen, on November 19th 1770, but later investigators believed that they had found evidence to show that he was born in the Royal Maternity Hospital, November 13th 1768. This is doubtful, however, and until further evidence is forthcoming it would seem reasonable to adhere to the date and year agreed upon by himself and his contemporaries. Thorvaldsen's father was an immigrant Icelandic woodcarver, *Gotskalk Thorvaldsen* by name, the son of a clergyman who came out of a good old family. His mother *Karen Dagnes,* was the daughter of a school teacher from Jutland. The story of Thorvaldsen's life was like a fairy tale, not very different from the career of Hans Andersen. It is the story of a little boy, born of poor parents, who attained the greatest esteem and rose to the highest position in society possible for a sculptor at that time; it is the story of the vast possibilities opening up for a boy who is born with a natural talent provided this talent is coupled with a firm character; and it is the story of what can be achieved by a person of natural aptitude if he is born at the right moment.

CHILDHOOD AND EARLY YEARS IN COPENHAGEN

Thorvaldsen's home was a poor one. His father was an indifferent wood-carver who had great difficulty in holding his own against his competitors, and he is reputed to have been a frequenter of the public houses of the town. In her

---

Thorvaldsen's christian name was actually Bertel (Danish for Bartholommeus). In Italy his name was – incorrectly – made into Alberto. He always adopted that name while staying abroad.

youth his mother is said to have been »a pretty little plump person". Thorvaldsen resembled her and she was very devoted to him. Later she became slovenly and neglected the home.

These facts influenced the boy's mind. At an early age the self-reliance and dogged tenacity which runs like a red cord through the whole of Thorvaldsen's life manifested itself. When only twelve years old Thorvaldsen assisted his father in his woodcarving work, and he soon surpassed him in skill. It is doubtful whether he received any regular schooling but as early as possible, in 1781, he entered the Royal Academy of Fine Arts, the lower classes of which were as that time intended for handicraft pupils. As Thorvaldsen grew older, became more skilled and obtained those Guild privileges which accompanied the awarding of the Academy's silver and gold medals, he thereby strengthened his father's position in the workshop and improved the family circumstances.

The Academy was well aware of Thorvaldsen's abilities. He had the sculptor *Johs. Wiedewelt* (professor of sculpture at the Academy) as his teacher. But he became the protégé of the most influential man in the Academy at the time, the painter *N. Abildgaard,* who made use of his assistance for the inside decorations of one of the Amalienborg Palaces (Amalienborg is the king's residence in Copenhagen). Thorvaldsen, then, was a pupil of the latter rather than that of his professor. His artistic training, which ended in 1793 with the award of the large gold medal, and his general development progressed haltingly and with some uncertainty. He required time to grow. Also, he had to work for his living by helping his father to carve figureheads for ships and mirror frames for the public, by drawing or modelling portraits and executing vignettes for books.

If the last few years before his departure abroad were a comparatively happy period, free as he was from financial worries, this was due to the work he did with his own hands.

The early works from Thorvaldsen's youth were all in the departing 18th century style, i.e. rococo with distinct classical traits. We have a number of reliefs from his hand, e.g. *The Seasons* and *The Times of the Day* (made for Amalienborg, in co-operation with Abildgaard), in which the classical influence is marked, and some portraits, especially the majestic rococo bust of the statesman A. P. Bernstorff, which won for him the favour of this powerful man. The importance of this period is the fact that the foundations of Thorvaldsen's personality were laid in those years. He was a dreamer, but in his childhood were sown the seeds of the worldly wisdom that later made him an excellent strategist in his dealings with the complications of life, and he accustomed himself to that constant application to his work which was characteristic for him to the end. Under the influence of outside pressure, a character was formed that was typically Scandinavian, and, more specifically, pronouncedly Danish. It was marked by a varying mood the changes of which were imperceptible, a combination of weakness and strength, without sharp edges, but with that perseverance which reaches its goal and is adamant when necessary. The keynote of Thorvaldsen's character was seriousness. As a young man he could not understand how a grown-up man could possibly laugh.

ROME 1797-1819

In 1796 Thorvaldsen was awarded the Academy's travelling studentship. Thanks to the influence of Bernstorff he was permitted to journey to Italy on H.M.S. "Thetis", a frigate commanded by Captain *Lorents Fisker*. He went on board on August 29th and arrived in Rome on March 8th, 1797. Later, Thorvaldsen celebrated this day as his "Roman Birthday".

The new surroundings made an enormous impression on him. It was a distinguishing trait in Thorvaldsen's character that he was possessed of an extreme receptiveness which made up for his educational deficiencies. He was described as being a searcher for knowledge, he drank in knowledge and new impressions, and fortunately for him wise and highly educated men helped him at the critical stages of his delveopment and gave him what support he needed.

His meeting in Rome with the painter *A. J. Carstens,* born in Holstein, proved important for his artistic development, but just as Abildgaard had been his mentor in his years at the Academy, so it was his countryman the antiquarian *Georg Zoëga,* Danish Envoy to the Papal Court, who gave him a sound knowledge of the ancient classical art and its spirit, and through his criticism he exercised a great influence upon Thorvaldsen's views. At the request of the Academy he taught himself to work in marble by studying and copying antique busts. He made a few other things, as for example a sketch of *Achilles with the dying Amazon Penthesilea,* which is among his most spiritual works. But he did not produce much. He was inwardly growing, and it was during these years that he developed into what he eventually became.

Such periods, marked by inactivity, were to occur time and again in Thorvaldsen's later life, but as was the case the first time his mind would then find an outlet with surprising ease and power when the time was opportune. This happened towards the close of his scholarship time in

Rome at the end of 1802 when, almost in desperation, he modelled his statue of *Jason*. It became a programme work. With it, he consummated the classical tendencies which had prevailed in Rome since the middle of the 18th century and through it he neared the style and spirit of the Græco-Roman ideals more than any other sculptor had done. The soil was to an exceptional degree ready for this work of his. The Italian sculptor *Canova,* the greatest name of the period, perceived and immediately acknowledged its significance, and this established Thorvaldsen's fame at one blow.

For reasons of economy, Thorvaldsen now had to decide to return to Denmark, but at the last moment the English aesthete and art-patron *Thomas Hope* commissioned him to execute *Jason* in marble and thus provided Thorvaldsen with the means to remain in Rome, which ensured his stay. Frederik VI's Denmark had been unable to finance the work of a great sculptor and to give him chances of development. Rome, however, was the "world's capital", where everybody converged, and where art lived on the orders placed by visiting patrons, especially rich English people. If Thorvaldsen gained renown through his own genius, England to a large extent financed it. Thorvaldsen soon received an abundance of commissions, and he remained in Rome until 1819, bound by a restless production. Unmoved by the great events of Napoleon's time, events which visited Rome in the form of war, plagues and rioting he created an art of lofty and eternal ideals characterized by human perfection and accomplished in accordance with the laws of beauty an harmony.

This period saw the completion of Thorvaldsen's most characteristic masterpieces. Amongst the statues are: *Cupid and Psyche* (1807), *Adonis* (1808), *Mars and Cupid,* a portrait statue of the little naked *Georgiana Russell* (1814-15), *Countess*

Ostermann, seated, dressed in Empire costume (1815), *Venus* (1813-16), *Hebe* (1816), *Ganymede with the Eagle* (1817), *Shepherd Boy* (1817), *Dancing Girl* (1817), *Mercury about to slay Argus* (1818), a standing statue of Madame *Bariatinsky*, which gives a characteristic picture of the female ideal of the time (1818), *Hope* (1817), *The Graces and Cupid* (1817-19), and the *Lion Monument, Lucerne* (1819).

Side by side with this he produced an abundance of reliefs. *Briseïs being led away from Achilles* (1803) proved as important for Thorvaldsen's handling of the relief style as his "Jason" had been for his treatment of statues. Later came *A genio lumen* (1808), the sepulchral monuments to *Auguste Böhmer* (ca. 1812) and *Bethmann-Hollweg* (1814) with the beautiful representations of the Genius of Death, *Night* and *Day* (1815), and *Priam supplicating Achilles for Hector's Body* (1815), which show his relief style at its height. His numerous *Scenes of Cupid's Exploits* began about 1809, but it was the frieze *The Triumphal Entry of Alexander the Great into Babylon* which established his fame. It was ordered for the decoration of the Quirinal Palace, Rome, to celebrate Napoleon's expected visit in 1812. Although it measures approximately 105 feet it took Thorvaldsen only three months to model it, and that under rather unfavourable conditions. His contemporaries were struck with amazement at this performance and honoured him by calling him "The Patriarch of Bas-Reliefs".

These works were to a great extent Thorvaldsen's contribution towards an interpretation of the artistic motifs of that time, and were often inspired by the statuary of antiquity, by Carstens or other artists, and not least by the rivalry existing between him and *Canova,* the great Italian sculptor. If Thorvaldsen did not appreciate Canova he was in some respects to take him for his model. They

mutually inspired one another, and in a number of works
they have both given solutions to the same subjects and
the same motifs. Outwardly, Thorvaldsen's activity developed along the same lines as Canova's, and just as Canova
founded and built a personal museum in his native town
of Possagno, Thorvaldsen himself conceived the idea of a
Thorvaldsen Museum. But Thorvaldsen, who was thir-
teen years Canova's junior, had a more highly developed
and more sensitive understanding of the Classical ideal in
sculpture and even felt drawn to the early Greek art, to the
Archaic art which at that time was not very well known and
not greatly valued. In 1816, he restored for King Ludwig
of Bavaria the gable group which had recently been excavated from the Aphaia Temple in Aegina (now in the Munic
Glyptotheca). Though the result is questionable from an
archaeological point of view this was one of his finest
artistic achievements. Also, he found in the Archaic art
the theme for *Hope,* which is at one time ancient Greek and
a romantic symbol.

This period saw, in Thorvaldsen, a growing appreciation
of the plastic values achieved by the classical age. It is
mainly Roman in *Adonis,* mainly Greek in *Hebe, Priam
supplicating Achilles for Hector's Body,* and *Hope.* This did
not prevent Thorvaldsen, however, from making use of
themes from everyday life as is seen in *Shepherd Boy* and
Mercury, and treating them in a manner that was not intrin-
sically diffrent from that of his other works. What pervaded
all Thorvaldsen's works was that true Danish nature of his
in all its emotional nuances. A true understanding of the
homogeneity of his works and his frequent ability to depict
symbols is not possible without keeping this in mind. However objectively he worked with plastic values and towards
the realisation of classical ideals there is hardly any doubt

that a large number of his works sprang from inner sources, viz. personal experiences, which crystallized symbolically in an artistic form as a sublimation of a specific mood.

The presence of German Romanticists in Rome probably played a part in preserving this lyrical strain in Thorvaldsen's character. His circle of acquaintances included German artists, some of which were occasionally his fellow-workers, and at one time he cultivated a type of drawing which was extremely near to the German Romantic school and very different from the other pencil and plaster sketches he left behind.

PERSONAL

Outwardly, Thorvaldsen had a brilliant career, inwardly he was to encounter great tribulations. The honours which were heaped upon him during his lifetime without affecting him in the least or changing his unsnobbish character began in 1804 when he was given the title of Professor of the Florence Academy. In 1805 he was made member as well as professor of the Copenhagen Academy; this was quite an unusual thing, and the appointment remained in abeyance until, 33 years later, he settled for good in Denmark. Also, in 1808, he became both member and professor of the San Luca Academy, a position of high standing and with an admirable salary. But in his private life he met with afflictions. His parents died before he had seen them again, and he never knew of lasting happiness in love. Early on, he fell in love with an Italian woman, *Anna Maria Magnani,* who was at that time the wife of the German archaeologist and Prussian minister to the Papal Court, Wilhelm Uhden. After she had been separated from her husband, he formed a liaison with her and they lived together for a number of years which were to be rather stormy. They could not get married because she was a Catholic. She gave birth to a son, probably in 1806, and in 1813 to a daughter, *Elisa*. The son's death, in 1811, affected Thorvaldsen deeply. In 1818, circles nearly connected with Thorvaldsen sought to bring about his engagement to a Scottish lady, Miss *Frances Mackenzie of Seaforth*. But Thorvaldsen severed all connections with her in a manner that did not do him credit. There was almost a scandal, and Thorvaldsen himself felt a sense of guilt which rankled in his heart for many years.

This and other adversities caused Thorvaldsen to decide, in 1819, to accede to ever growing requests from Danish quarters to return home. His assistance was thought desirable for the decorating of C. F. Hansen's new buildings. Christiansborg Palace, the Palace Church, the Court-House, and the Church of Our Lady, all in Copenhagen. On July 14th 1819 he left Rome. The journey became a veritable progress of honour. It received wide mention in the Press of the day, and during his progress through Italy, Germany and Poland he received many commissions and signed many contracts for the execution of several important monuments. In Copenhagen where he was fêted to a degree, he modelled the Royal family and arranged to execute the group *The Sermon of John the Baptist* for the pediment of the Church of Our Lady and the *Twelve Apostles* for the interior of the church. On December 16th 1820 he was back in Rome again.

ROME 1820-38

Thorvaldsen's activities had gradually increased, and when he returned with the vast number of important commissions he had received, this development gathered speed and his studio became a workshop turning out objects of art by wholesale, as it were. Here many marble carvers and young artists were employed, engaged upon work after his designs and under his supervision. Daily he would walk about correcting and guiding and taking a hand whenewer he thought it necessary. Several marble replicas were made, even of his large statues, and it is said about the bust of the *Emperor Alexander I,* for instance, which he modelled in Warsaw in 1820 that he received so many commissions for this that on his return to Rome a couple of Thorvaldsen's marble workers were engaged on this bust alone for several years. His studio at this time was one of the sights of Rome, which all tourists of any consequence simply had to see— and this often meant new commissions. But Thorvaldsen's competence in building up this business and administrating it without any working capital, and infusing his assistants with his own spirit are other remarkable features of his talent.

The large monuments which maintain Thorvaldsen's name and reputation abroad were executed in the 'twenties and 'thirties. For Poland he executed the Count *W. Potoĉki* monument in the Cracow cathedral (1821), *Copernicus* (1823) and the equestrian statue of Prince *Josef Poniatowski,* which is the Polish National Monument (1826-27), both in Warsaw. For Germany were executed the Duke of *Leuchtenberg* (1827) and the equestrian statue of the Elector *Maximilian* (1833-35), both in Munich; *Gutenberg* in Mayence, modelled by H. V. Bissen after Thorvaldsen's design (1833-34), *Schiller* in Stuttgart, a true Poet's Statue, and one of Thorvaldsen's most important works (1835). A sketch for a contemplated Goethe monument, however, came to nothing. For Italy were executed the painter *Appiani's* monument for the Brera Gallery in Milan with the large, superb relief of the *Three Graces* (1821), the statue of *Conradin,* the last Hohenstaufen emperor, commissioned by King Ludwig of Bavaria for the Sta. Maria del Carmine Church in Naples (1836), and the monument of *Pope Pius VII* at St. Peter's, ordered and paid for by Cardinal Consalvi (1824-31). The last mentioned is a striking proof of Thorvaldsen's renown, and it is a unique thing for a heretic to have been permitted to execute a papal monument for this stronghold of Catholicism. England received the statue of *Byron,* Cambridge (1831). But Thorvaldsen's most comprehensive work was the *decoration of the Church of Our Lady, Copenhagen,* which included the statue of Christ (1821). the Twelve Apostles (1821-27 and 1842), the John the Baptist Group (1821-22), the baptismal font (The Kneeling Angel, 1828) and the two relief friezes of the Road to Calvary and the Entry into Jerusalem (both 1839-40).

To all these may be added occasional works, a multitude of reliefs as for instance the majority of his Cupid series, *The Ages of Love* (1824), the two extraordinary representations of the *Hylas* legend (1831 and 1833), the four round allegories of *The Ages of Life and the Seasons of the Year* (1836) and *Hector saying Farewell to Andromache* (1837). Many people from abroad wished to be modelled by Thorvaldsen and this called the vast number of busts from his hand into existence which only recently have been valued as they deserve.

The most important feature of this period is his Christian sculptures. His contemporaries were surprised that the Greek, Thorvaldsen, should master Christian art as well, but his style was actually to set the standard in this field almost up to the present day; the miraculous simplicity of the posture motif places his figure of Christ and his Angel of Baptism in the front rank amongst his masterpieces. Altogether his statue of Christ is the only representation of Christ that has been able to gather around it people of all nations. It contains the essence of all religion, embodying as it does love of Mankind and love of all that lives.

2*

OLD AGES IN DENMARK

After twenty years of intense activity Thorvaldsen acceded
to pleas from Denmark to take up his permanent residence
there. The Government sent a warship, the frigate "Rota"
under Captain *H. B. Dahlerup,* to fetch him and on the
8th August 1838 he went on board the ship at Leghorn.
On the 17th September he saw Copenhagen again. His
return became a national event of almost legendary character.

To avoid the overwhelming idolizing he encountered
everywhere and escape the social duties this involved he
accepted Baroness *Stampe's* invitation to come to Nysø,
near Præstø. Once more he paid a visit to Italy lasting from
May 1841 to October 1842, but apart from that he shared
his time between his official residence, Charlottenborg,
where in 1843 he modelled the colossal statue of *Hercules*
for Christiansborg, and Nysø. Here, he had peace to work
in the studio which was built for him in the beautiful grounds
and where he executed his *Self-portrait* (a statue) (1839) and
the two reliefs containing scenes of his own and the family
Stampe's everyday life at Nysø (1840)–and not only did
he find peace to work, but, after his lifelong uncomfortable
bachelor's existence, he found a home, and his conversations
with Baroness Stampe gave him an opportunity to take
his life under review. His striving soul had found peace. He
died suddenly in the Theatre Royal, Copenhagen, on the
24th March 1844, and on the 6th September 1848 his coffin
was lowered into the grave prepared for him in the courtyard of the Museum.

EPITAPH

Thorvaldsen influenced Danish art through his pupil H. V.
Bissen and Vilhelm Bissen (son of the latter), and this
influence lasted, roughly speaking, up to the time of Kai

Nielsen and Utzon-Frank. A consequence of this was that Danish sculpture never lost its sure and sober objectiveness, not even during the wildest naturalistic experiments. It is obvious that an artist who has been so enthusiastically acclaimed as Thorvaldsen must later become subject to divergent estimates. With his fine sense of rhythm, with his superior artistic instinct and his ability to transform human feelings into sculptural postures and linear composition he has, however, shown the Danish mentality in such a sublime manner that people of other nations have been enabled to understand and appreciate its distinctive traits. For our age, his significance lies more in the fact that he was Danish than in the fact that he personified the peak of Roman classicism. Through its example of restraint and artistic tact, his art has preserved its power over the human mind and retained its importance as a regulator that balances our artistic development. The story of his life possesses a moral power which is both a model and a spur. Even recently it has become apparent that his art still concerns us because of his keen sense of the beauty of the human body.

SIGURD SCHULTZ

LITERATURE ON THORVALDSEN
AND THE MUSEUM

There exists a very comprehensive literature on Thorvaldsen, but only a few books can find mention here.

A historical survey and valuation of Thorvaldsen's life and work may be found in *Just Mathias Thiele's* "Thorvaldsens Biographi", I-IV, Copenhagen 1851-56 (German edition I-III, Leipzig 1852-56; abridged English edition, London 1865), which is still the most authoritative work on the subject. The last complete monograph, "Thorvaldsen" I-III, Copenhagen 1924-30, was published by *Th. Oppermann* (Director of the Museum 1921-32). In French appeared *Eugène Plon:* "Thorvaldsen", Paris 1867 (Italien edition, Florence 1874; English edition, London 1874 and Boston 1874; German edition, Vienna 1875). Published in German, Adolf Rosenberg's "Thorvaldsen", Bielefeld and Leipzig 1896 (Künstler-Monographien, hrsg. von H. Knackfuss, XVI). For the general public in Denmark, *Erik Moltesen* wrote his conscientious book: "Thorvaldsens Museum", Copenhagen 1927; and *Knud V. Rosenstand* a popular, easily read book: "Bertel Thorvaldsen" 2nd edition, Copenhagen 1932. In this book the author tries, among other things, to shed light on Thorvaldsen's personality by means of the characteristic anecdotes about Thorvaldsen which have been handed down to us.

Contemporary descriptions of Thorvaldsen's personality are to be found in *C. F. Wilckens:* "Træk af Thorvaldsens Konstner- og Omgangsliv", Copenhagen 1874 (German edition 1875), an entertaining book, which must, however, be read critically. It is written by Thorvaldsen's valet. Further, *Alex. Wilde:* "Erindringer om Jerichau og Thorvaldsen ombord paa Fregatten Rota 1838", Copenhagen

1884, and Baroness *Christine Stampe*'s: "Erindringer om
Thorvaldsen", Copenhagen 1912, which is one of the standard works. Traits aimed at throwing light upon the admira-
tion shown Thorvaldsen by his contemporaries have been
collected by *Sigurd Schultz* in his book: "Da Thorvaldsen
kom hjem", Copenhagen 1938. Important contributions
to the understanding of Thorvaldsen's personality are contained in *Rikard Magnussen:* "Thorvaldsens Livsanskuelse",
Copenhagen 1936 and *Louis Bobé:* "Thorvaldsen i Kærlig-
hedens Aldre", Copenhagen 1938.

As regards the art of Thorvaldsen *Julius Lange*'s "Sergel
og Thorvaldsen", Copenhagen 1886 (German edition,
Berlin 1894) is still a classic. A comprehensive collection
of illustrations, with explanatory captions is contained
in *Emil Hannover*'s: "Thorvaldsens Værker", Copenhagen
1907. *Albert Repholtz:* "Thorvaldsen og Nysø", Copenhagen 1911 and "Thorvaldsens Tegninger", Copenhagen
1920 by the same author, and *Johannes V. Jensen* and *Aage
Marcus:* "Thorvaldsens Portrætbuster", Copenhagen 1926
deal with special subjects. The finest analysis of the ability
Thorvaldsen possessed to give his experiences symbolic
expression in his works has been given by *Johannes V. Jensen*
in the introductory pages of the lastmentioned work, and
in an essay called "Thorvaldsens Fristelser", to be found in
his book "Form og Sjæl", Copenhagen 1931. A modern
appreciation of Thorvaldsen is to be found in *Chr. Elling:*
"Thorvaldsen", Copenhagen 1944.

The origin of the Museum building is given in a book
by *Chr. Bruun* and *L. P. Fenger:* "Thorvaldsens Musæums
Historie", Copenhagen 1892; this is one of the authoritative
works. A careful, descriptive catalogue of the collections
of the Museum was published by its first curator, the numis-
matist and archæologist, lic. theol. *Ludvig Müller,* whose cat-

aloguing of the collections deserves high praise. The book is called "Thorvaldsens Museum", I-v, Copenhagen 1847-50 (French edition partie 1-5, 1847-51); it was a standard work at the time and even to-day forms the basis for the cataloguing of the Museum. The most comprehensive work in this category is still the popular and instructive guide to the Museum, *M. Galschiøtt:* "Thorvaldsens Museum", Copenhagen 1895, which has unfortunately for a long time been unobtainable from the book-shops.

In addition to the current catalogues, the Thorvaldsen Museum has published a list of the engraved stones that the Museum possesses, viz. "Catalogue of the Antique Engraved Gems and Cameous", by Poul Fossing (Copenhagen 1929). Also, the Museum publish, at intervals, "Meddelelser fra Thorvaldsens Museum" (which have so far been published in the years 1917, 1918, 1929, 1931, 1935, 1938, 1944, 1947, 1948, 1952); the "Meddelelser" contain articles about Thorvaldsen's works, the Museum building, etc.

*   *   *

REGARDING THE USE OF
THE CATALOGUE

The present guide book is arranged room by room, the numbers of which are usually to be found in the window niches.

The year given for the creation of the sculpture is always that of the modelling. If nothing to the contrary is stated it is to be understood that the works by Thorvaldsen himself have been executed in Rome. It is also stated whether the work in question is an original model, a cast or a marble.

If a marble is known, or can be assumed, to have been executed under Thorvaldsen's supervision or, possibly, been retouched by him, his name is added in a parenthesis. In the case of the marble replicas executed after Thorvaldsen's death the name of the artist (if known) responsible for the execution is indicated in a parenthesis.

Based on information contained in Chr. Bruun's and L. P. Fenger's "Thorvaldsens Musæums Historie", pp. 105, 109-10, 114-15 and copies of the accounts of the Museum, explanations of the motifs decorating the ceiling of each room, together with the names of the participating artists have as far as possible been included.

*

Dr. phil. Vagn Poulsen and Dr. phil. P. J. Riis have very kindly assisted in the cataloguing of the antique collections.

* * *

GROUND FLOOR

ENTRANCE GALLERY

The ceiling reliefs are executed by G. Chr. Freund and Fr. G. Hertzog
from designs by Thorvaldsen. G. Hoffmann and the architects
Jens J. Eckersberg and T. Sørensen have also assisted.

STATUES

113 Nicolaus Copernicus. Original model. 1823. Erected in bronze in Warsaw 1830. Removed by the Germans during the War 1939-45, but restored by the Poles and re-erected in 1950.

114-16 Gutenberg. On the base: Invention of movable types (115) and of the printing press (116). Original models. Modelled 1833-34 by H. V. Bissen on Thorvaldsen's instruction and under his supervision. Erected in bronze in Mayence 1837.

123 Equestrian statue of Prince Jozef Poniatowski. Original model. Commissioned in 1817; final contract in 1820. Modelled 1826-27. Cast in bronze, the statue was to have been erected in Warsaw in 1832. Emperor Nicholas I refused to allow this and presented it to General Paskiewicz, who had it erected on his estate, Homel, in the province of Mohilew, Russia. In 1922 it was returned to Warsaw, when it was erected in the Saxon Square and unveiled, on May 3rd 1923, with great ceremony. On December 16th 1944 it was destroyed by the Germans before they left the city. A

new bronze statue, cast from the original model in the Museum, was presented to the City of Warsaw by the Danish State and the City Corporation of Copenhagen, and unveiled in the Lazienki Park, Warsaw, on the 23rd February, 1952.

128   Equestrian statue of Maximilian, Elector of Bavaria. The horse is an original model, whereas the rider is a cast, purchased in 1855. Modelled in 1833-35. Erected in bronze in Munich, 1839.

135-37   Schiller. The Apotheosis of the Poet (135), The Genius of Poetry (136), and the Goddess of Victory (137) appear on the base. Original models. (The statue itself was acquired by the Museum in 1857). Modelled 1835. Erected in bronze in Stuttgart, 1839.

142-145   Pope Pius VII. On the sides: two female figures representing Heavenly Wisdom (143) and Divine Strength (144). On the base: the Papal Arms, supported by two angels (145). Original models. 1824-31. Erected 1831 in marble in St. Peter's, Rome.

156   Engène de Beauharnais, Duke of Leuchtenberg, Napoleon I's stepson, Viceroy of Italy. Original model. 1827. Erected in marble on the tomb of the Duke in St. Michael's Church, Munich, 1830.

BUSTS

212   Count Adam Moltke of Nütschau. Original model. The winter of 1803-04.

219   Baron Herman Schubart, Danish Envoy to Italy. 1804. Marble (Thorvaldsen).

220   Baroness Jacoba Elisabeth Schubart. 1804. Marble (Thorvaldsen).

253   The painter Horace Vernet. Marble (H. V. Bissen). See No. 254 (page 36).

258 Sir Thomas Maitland, Lord-High-Commissioner of the Ionian Islands. Original model. 1818. Erected in bronze on the island of Zante. Relief No. 600 (see below), also in bronze, was on the base of the monument. During the war of 1939-45, both works were removed by the Italians. The relief was later re-found.

304 Princess Eudoxia Galitzin. Winter 1803-04. Marble (Thorvaldsen).

RELIEFS

317 Hercules receiving the Wine of Immortality from Hebe. Original model. With Nos. 318-320 modelled in 1807-10 for Christiansborg Palace, Copenhagen.

318 Hygeia feeding the Serpent of Aesculapius. Original model. See No. 317.

319 Minerva giving a Soul to the Man made by Prometheus. Original model. See No. 317.

320 Nemesis reading the Deeds of Mankind to Jupiter. Original model. See No. 317.

503 FRIEZE. Triumphant Entry of Alexander the Great into Babylon. Cast. Modelled in 1812 for the Quirinal Palace to celebrate the expected visit of Napoleon to Rome.

530 The Genius of Government. Original model. 1837.

531 The Genius of Justice. Like preceding No. intended for the Maximilian monument in Munich; not used. Original model. 1837.

600 Minerva protecting Virtue, whilst exposing Vice. Original model. 1818. See No. 258 (above).

CORRIDOR

Ceiling decoration: blue vault of stars divided by bands with the 12 signs of Zodiac, painted by Heinrich Hansen. The signs of the Zodiac are the work of Fr. G. Hertzog. Carl Løffler and E. Fich have also assisted.

STATUES

5   Mercury about to slay Argus. Original model. 1818.

7   Mars and Cupid. Original model. Remodelled from a statue of the peace-bringing Mars which was modelled in 1808 and is now only known from J. M. Thiele's book, "Bertel Thorvaldsen og hans Værker" I, Copenhagen 1831, Panel XXXIII.

9   Vulcan. Original model. 1838.

29   The Graces and Cupid. Original model. 1817-19.

52   Jason with the Golden Fleece. Thorvaldsen's first major work. Original model. 1802-03.

53   Adonis. Original model. 1808.

55-56 Two Caryatids. Casts. Modelled in 1813 for a monument in Warsaw. Marble copies erected 1826 in the Throne Room in Christiansborg Palace, were destroyed by the fire of 1884.

59-70 The Sermon of John the Baptist. 1821-22. In bronze over the main entrance to the Church of Our Lady, Copenhagen. The figures: 63, an old Scribe; 64, a Youth; 66, a Pharisee; 68, the Boy and the Girl; and 70, the reclining Shepherd, are all original models.

71   Roman Warrior, standing. Original model. Originally intended for inclusion in the John the Baptist group.

72   A Jew, seated. Original model. Originally intended for inclusion in the John the Baptist group.

110 The Angel of Baptism. Original model. 1823. (Represents angel in standing position. A marble replica to be found in the National Museum, Stockholm).

119   A Lion dying over the Royal Shield of the French King. Hewn in enormous size in a wall rock at Lucerne to commemorate the Swiss who were killed in Paris during the revolutions of August 10th, September 2nd and 3rd, 1792. 1819. Cast. Hewn in the rock by Lucas Ahorn of Constance. Work completed in 1821.

122   Couching Lion. Original model. 1825.

125   Horse. Modelled for the monument to Poniatowski. Used in Victory's Quadriga (made by H. V. Bissen) on the roof of the Museum. Partly original model. 1822-23.

129   Horse. Modelled for the monument to Maximilian of Bavaria. Partly original model. 1832-33.

146   Angel. Original model. 1830. Erected in marble on the monument to Pope Pius VII in St. Peter's, Rome.

147   Angel. Original model. 1830. See No. 146.

155   Count Wlodzimierz Potočki. Original model. 1821. In marble on the Count's sepulchral monument in the cathedral on Wawell hill, Cracow. See No. 627 (page 34).

162   Thorvaldsen leaning on his statue of "Hope". Modelled at Nysø 1839. Cast. See No. 46 in Room VIII.

BUSTS

186   St. Apollinaris. Bishop, patron saint of Ravenna. Original model. 1821.

187   Leonardo Pisano, the mathematician (1180-1250). Marble (Thorvaldsen).

189   Maximilian I, Elector of Bavaria. Original model. 1831.

205   Prince Frederik of Augustenburg. 1819. Marble. (Thorvaldsen).

211 Count Conrad Rantzau-Breitenburg, Danish states-
     man. Original model. 1805.

221A Jacob Baden, Professor of the Copenhagen Univer-
     sity. 1806. Marble (Thorvaldsen). Purchased 1924.

223 Thorvaldsen, self-portrait. 1810. Cast from the
     marble replica, made by Thorvaldsen himself, in the
     Royal Academy of Fine Arts, Copenhagen.

233 King Ludwig I of Bavaria as Crown Prince. Original
     model. 1818.

240A Chr. August Tiedge, German Poet. The winter of
     1805–06. Marble (Thorvaldsen). Purchased 1920.

240B Elisa von der Recke, German Poetess. The winter of
     1805–06. Marble (Thorvaldsen). Purchased 1920.

247 The Grand Duchess Helene of Russia. Original model.
     1829.

252 Napoleon being apotheosized as Emperor. 1830.
     Marble (Thorvaldsen). Purchased 1929.

255 Sir Walter Scott. 1832. Cast.

256 Lord Byron. 1817. Marble.

267 Lady Louisa Sandwich. Original model. 1816.

268 "Miss Lucan", daughter of Richard Bingham, 2. Earl
     of Lucan. Original model. 1821.

270 Pope Pius VII. Original model. 1824.

271 Cardinal Ercole Consalvi. Original model. 1824.

275 Georg Wilhelm Karl Wilding, Prince of Butera
     and Radali. 1815. Marble (Thorvaldsen). Purchased
     1950.

276 Donna Catherina di Branciforte, Princess Butera,
     Consort of the above. 1815. Marble (Thorvaldsen).
     Purchased 1950.

280 Ghazi 'L-Din Haidar, Padshah of Oudh. Original
     model 1824.

283 Dr. John Wyllie. Original model. 1831. To be found

in marble, in the Town Hall of Forfar, Angusshire, Scotland.

303   Portrait of a Man. Original model.

RELIEFS

361   Victory. Intended for the base of the Potočki-monument (See No. 155, page 29); not used. Partly original model. 1830.

363   Victory. Original model. 1830.

420   Venus, Mars and Cupid in Vulcan's Workshop. Mars original model. The rest casts. Remodelling of No. 419 in Room IX.

423   Leda and the Swan. Original model. Nysø 1841.

487   The Sea Goddess Thetis dipping her son Achilles in the Styx. Original model. 1837.

491   Briseïs being led away from Achilles by the Heralds of Agamemnon. Original model. 1837.

500   Hector, in Helen's Chamber, upbraids Paris for his Cowardice. Original model. 1837.

504   Alexander in his triumphal chariot being received by the Goddess of Peace. Variant of the centre-piece of the frieze, Alexander's Procession. Used for the marble replica of the frieze in Count Sommariva's Villa, now Villa Carlotta, on Lake Como (see No. 505). Original model.

505   FRIEZE. Triumphal Entry of Alexander the Great into Babylon. A variant of the frieze in the entrance gallery (see No. 503, page 27). Cast. Executed in marble in Thorvaldsen's studio on the commision of Count Sommariva for his Villa, now Villa Carlotta, Lake Como. The centre-piece with Alexander is, however, not the same as in the marble replica in the Villa Carlotta (see No. 504).

506-7   Parts of the frieze, Alexander's Procession. Used for the marble replica of the frieze erected in Christiansborg Palace, Copenhagen. 506, Cast. 507, original model. 1831.

516   Thaïs luring Alexander to set Persepolis on fire. Remodelling of No. 515 (page 61). Original model. 1837.

526   The Genius of Poetry. Intended for the Schiller Monument (see No. 135-37, page 26). Original model. 1835.

529   The Genius of Peace and Freedom. Original model. Copenhagen 1844.

551   Adam and Eve with Cain and Abel. Original model. 1838.

567   The twelve-year-old Christ teaching in the Temple. Original model. Nysø 1841.

568   Christ and the Woman of Samaria at the Well. Original model. Nysø 1841.

575-78   The four Evangelists borne by the Winged Figures used to symbolize them. 1833. Marble.

583   Luke with his symbol, the Ox. Original model.

584   Luke, as the first Christian painter. Original model.

589   Yuletide Joy in Heaven. Nysø 1842. Cast.

603   The clergyman, Hans Madsen before Johan Rantzau. Original model. Nysø 1841. In bronze in Svanninge Church, Funen.

SEPULCHRAL RELIEFS

593-595   Angels of the Last Judgment. Original models. 1842

611   Raphael being garlanded by the Goddess of Victory, the Genius of Art holding a Torch. Intended, but not used, for the Raphael monument in the Pantheon, Rome. Original model. 1833.

612 Cardinal Consalvi leading the Papal Provinces back to Pius VII. Original model. Like the bust No. 271 (page 30) to be found in marble on Consalvi's sarcophagus in the Pantheon. Erected in 1824.

613 Tobias healing his blind Father. Original model. 1828. Executed in marble for the memorial to the ophthalmologist, Vacca Berlinghieri in Campo Santo, Pisa.

616 Brother and Sister leaving their Mother on Earth. Original model. 1835. Executed in marble for the memorial to Princess Helena Poninska's children in the Palace Chapel, Czerwonogród (Podolia).

618 Baron Schubart bidding Farewell to his dying Wife. Original model. 1814. Executed in marble for the memorial to Baroness Jacoba Elisabeth Schubart. (See Room XI, No. 618 A).

620 A Man Extending his Hand to his Veiled Wife. Original model. C. 1831-32. Executed in marble for the memorial to Sir Charles Drake Garrard, Esquire of Lamer, in the church in Wheathampstead, Hertfordshire, England.

621 Mother leaving her Son who is carried off by the Genius of Death. Original model. 1816. Executed in marble for the memorial to Countess Borkowska in the Dominican Church, Lwôw.

622 The Genius of Death by a sepulchral Monument at the foot of which an elderly Woman is kneeling. 1818. Cast. Executed in marble for Countess Newburgh as a memorial to her husband, Anthony Radcliffe, 5th Earl of Newburgh, in the Catholic church in Slindon, Sussex, England.

623 An elderly Woman kneeling between two Angels. Original model. 1828. Executed in marble for the

3*

memorial to Lady Lawley in the church in Escrick, Yorkshire, England.

624 A Woman, floating over the Genius of Death, and ascending to Heaven. Original model. 1818. Executed in marble on the tomb of Baroness Chaudoir.

625 Similar work to No. 624. Original model.

627 The Genius of Death. Original model. 1829. Executed in marble for the memorial to Count Wlodzimierz Potočki in the cathedral on Wawell hill, Cracow (see No. 155, page 29).

*

At the entrance to the Christ Hall is a model showing the *stages of a work of sculpture,* from the rack and the modelling in clay, casting in plaster (with the socalled sham-form) to the hewing in stone. Below is a complete set of sculpturing implements for work in clay, plaster and stone.

CHRIST HALL

The vault decoration is based on a design from the Pompeian Baths.

STATUES

82 Christ. 1821. Cast from the original model. Erected in marble in the Church of Our Lady, Copenhagen, 1839.

86-108 The Twelwe Apostles. 86, Peter. 87, Matthew. 89, John. 91, James the Less. 93, Philip. 96, Thomas. 98, James the Greater. 99, Bartholomew. 101, Simon Zelotes. 103, Paul. 105, Thaddeus. 108, Andrew. Original models, executed in 1821-27, with the exception of Thaddeus and Andrew which were modelled in 1841-42. Nos. 86-103 erected in marble in the Church of Our Lady, Copenhagen, in 1839; 105 and 108 were added later and were handed over to the church in 1848.

112 The Angel of Baptism. C. 1828. Cast. Erected in marble in the Church of our Lady, Copenhagen, in 1839.

RELIEFS

559 FRIEZE. Christ's Entry into Jerusalem. Original model. Nysø 1839-40. Preliminary work for the frieze over the main entrance to the Church of Our Lady, Copenhagen.

560 FRIEZE. Christ in his way to Calvary. Original model. Nysø 1839-40. Preliminary work for the Choir of the Church of Our Lady, Copenhagen.

564 Christ entrusting the Government of the Church to the Apostle Peter. 1818. In marble on the front of the communion table in the Palace Chapel, Villa Poggio Imperiale, near Florence. Cast of this marble work.

569 The Annunciation. Original model. 1842.

570 The Adoration of the Shepherds. Original model. 1842.

572 The twelve-year-old Christ teaching in the Temple. Original model. 1842.

573 St. John baptizing Christ. Original model. 1842.

596 The Child's Guardian Angel. Original model. Copenhagen 1838. Executed in marble for the School-children's Poor-box in the Church of Our Lady. Copenhagen.

597 Christian Charity. 1810. Marble. Executed in marble for the Poor-box in the Church of Our Lady, Copenhagen.

ROOM I

The ceiling decoration is designed and executed by A. F. Behrends. M. M.
Goldschmidt, E. Fich, J. J. G. Guntzelnick and J. P. Rasmussen have
also assisted. The theme is taken from a Pompeian glass amphora and a
floor mosaic in Goethe's House.

40   STATUE. Ganymede offering the brimming Bowl. 1804.
     Marble (Thorvaldsen). Purchased in London 1920.

42   — Ganymede filling the Drinking Bowl. 1816. Mar-
     ble. A marble replica from Thorvaldsen's workshop
     is in the Hermitage, Leningrad.

224 BUST. The painter, C. W. Eckersberg. 1816. Marble
     (Thorvaldsen). Presented by Eckersberg's daughters,
     1883.

254 — The painter, Horace Vernet. Original model. 1832.
     The original marble is in the Calvet Museum at
     Avignon.

284 — Portrait of a Man. Original model.

285 — Portrait of a Man. Original model.

327 RELIEF. The Genius of Light with Pegasus. Original
     model. C. 1836.

517 — Art and the light-bringing Genius. Original model.
     Considered to be the preliminary work for No.
     518 (page 61).

548 — The Genius of the New Year. Nysø 1840. Cast.

ROOM II

The ceiling decoration, composed by Chr. Købke, is based on a theme
from Diomedes' Villa in Pompeii. It is executed by Købke in co-operation
with J. F. Busch and E. Fich.

27   GROUP. Cupid and Psyche, re-united in Heaven.
     1807. Marble (H. V. Bissen).

426 RELIEF. The Ages of Love. 1824. Marble.
428 — Cupid leaving the Couch of the sleeping Psyche.
     Original model. Nysø 1841.
429 — Psyche, with her Lamp, approaching the sleeping
     Cupid. Original model. Nysø 1841.
430 — Cupid reviving the fainting Psyche. Montenero,
     1810. Marble (Thorvaldsen). Purchased in London,
     1926.
585 — Angels, singing. 1833. Marble.
587 — Angels, playing instruments. 1833. Marble.

ROOM III

*The decoration of the ceiling is the work of Ludv. Lehmann, Joel Ballin,
J. J. G. Guntzelnick and J. F. Busch. Lehmann has painted Aurora
leading the Horses of the Sun, the four floating figures, the four quarters
of the globe and the triumph of Galathea, in the lunette. Ballin has
executed the stucco frieze from a motif on an antique bronze pail.*

29A GROUP. The Graces and Cupid. Modelled 1817-19.
     Marble (Thorvaldsen). Purchased 1952.
245 BUST. Karoline von Rehfues. Original model. 1827.
305 — Portrait of a Lady. Original model.
340 RELIEF. The Dance of the Muses on Helicon. Modelled
     at the Villa Montenero, Leghorn (1804). Re-
     modelled 1816. Marble (H. V. Bissen).
371 — Cupid feeding Hygeia's Serpent. 1837. Marble.
375 — Cupid, fettered, with the Graces. 1831. Marble.
393 — Cupid pleading with Jupiter to make the Rose the
     Queen of Flowers. 1831. Marble.
396 — Cupid caressing the faithful Dog. 1831. Marble.
397 — Cupid making a Butterfly Net–a symbol of the
     Soul or the fleeting Heart. 1831. Marble.

ROOM IV

*The ceiling decoration: Chr. Købke has executed the four medallions
from Thorvaldsen's compositions on the story of Cupid and Psyche. The
other figures are the work of Fr. G. Hertzog. N. Borggreen, William
Hammer and Ph. Aug. Fischer have designed and executed the ornaments.
The frieze is from a terra-cotta in Pompeii.*

11 STATUE. Venus with the Apple, the prize of beauty
     awarded by Paris. 1813-16. Marble (Thorvaldsen).
     Purchased in London, 1920.

348 RELIEF. Venus born of the Foam. Original model. 1809.

388 — Cupid as the Tamer of the Lion. Original model.
     1809.

409A — Cupid with Bacchus. 1810. Marble (Th. Stein).

410 — Cupid with a Swan and Boys Plucking Fruit –
     Summer. Montenero. 1810. Marble.

412 — Cupid and the young Bacchus trampling Grapes
     under Foot–Autumn. From Anacreon's 17th song.
     Montenero, 1810. Marble.

414 — Cupid received by Anacreon–Winter. From Ana-
     creon's 3rd song. 1823. Marble (Thorvaldsen). The
     same poem inspired Hans Andersen to write the fairy
     story "The Naugthy Boy". Presented by Thorvald-
     sen to Thomas Hope in 1828. Purchased in England
     1917.

ROOM V

*The ceiling decoration is designed by William Hammer, who has also
executed the wreaths. Chr. Købke has modelled Apollo's Victory over
Marsyas in the centre panel as well as the seven smaller panels,
the sacrificing genii, the masks, etc.*

51 STATUE. Jason with the Golden Fleece. Modelled
     1802-3. Commissioned by Thomas Hope in 1803

and executed in marble in Rome by Thorvaldsen; completed in 1828. Bought 1917 at the Hope sale in England and included in the Museum in 1920.

249 BUST. Prince Jozef Poniatowski. Original model. 1819.

286 — Portrait of a Man. Original model.

489 RELIEF. Briseïs being led away from Achilles by the Heralds of Agamemnon. 1803. Marble (H. V. Bissen).

492A — Priam supplicating Achilles for Hector's Body. 1815. Marble (C. Peters).

493 — Achilles bandaging the wounds of Patroclus. 1837. Marble.

495 — Achilles with the slain Amazon Penthesilea. 1837. Marble.

ROOM VI

In the ceiling decoration, Chr. Købke has painted the centre panel with a motif from Nero's Golden House (formerly called Titus' Baths). The ornamentation is the work of A. P. Madsen.

38 STATUE. Hebe. 1816. Marble (Thorvaldsen). Purchased in London, 1938.

265A BUST. Henry Hope, eldest son of Thomas Hope. Presumably modelled in 1821. Marble (Thorvaldsen). Bought 1917 at the Hope sale in England.

266A — Younger Son of Thomas Hope. Presumably modelled in the winter of 1816-17. Marble (Thorvaldsen). Bought 1917 at the Hope sale in England.

321 RELIEF. Hercules and Hebe. Marble.

322 — Aesculapius and Hygeia. Marble.

323 — Minerva and Prometheus. Marble.

324 RELIEF. Nemesis and Jupiter. Marble.

(321-324 were modelled in 1807-10 for Christiansborg
       Palace, Copenhagen).

ROOM VII

The reliefs in the ceiling decoration are modelled by G. Chr. Freund.
The ornaments on the dark ground are the work of A. P. Madsen.

  6 GROUP. Mars and Cupid. From Anacreon's 45th
       song. Remodelled from a statue of the peace-
       bringing Mars, which was modelled in 1808 and
       is now only known from J. M. Thiele's book,
       "Bertel Thorvaldsen og hans Værker", I, Copen-
       hagen 1831, Panel XXXIII. Marble (H. V. Bissen).

273 BUST. Count G. B. Sommariva, Italian Politician and
       Art Collector. Original model. C. 1817-18.

287 — Portrait of a Man. Original model.

486 RELIEF. Perseus carrying off Andromeda on Pegasus.
       Nysø 1839. Cast.

499A — Hector with Paris and Helen. 1809. Marble (H. V.
       Bissen).

501A — Hector saying Farewell to Andromache. 1837.
       Marble (H. V. Bissen and Vilh. Bissen). Presented
       by J. C. Jacobsen, Esq.

502 — Homer singing to the People. Original model. 1836.

ROOM VIII

The Bacchic scenes on the ceiling are modelled by G. Chr. Freund.
The ornaments on the dark ground are the work of W. Hammer.

 46 STATUE. The Goddes of Hope with a Fruit Blossom
       in her Hand. 1817. Marble (H. V. Bissen).

366 RELIEF. The Fates with the Thread of Life. Original model. 1833.

367 — Night with her Children, Sleep and Death. 1815. Marble.

368 — Day: Aurora with the Genius of Light. 1815. Marble.

402 — Cupid gathering Shells for an Ornament. Original model. 1831.

403 — Cupid calling forth Flowers from Stony Ground. Original model. 1831.

ROOM IX

The figures in the ceiling decoration are executed by G. Chr. Freund and the ornaments by C. F. Sørensen and C. Weber.

8 STATUE. Vulcan. 1838. Marble (H. V. Bissen).

237 BUST. Wilhelm von Humboldt, German Statesman and Philologist. Original model. 1808.

288 — Portrait of a Man. Original model.

374 RELIEF. The Dancing Graces. Original model.

418 — Cupid complaining to Venus of a Beesting. From Anacreon's 40th song. Original model. Remodelling of No. 417, Room XIV.

419 — The Forging of Cupid's Arrows in Vulcan's Smithy. From Anacreon's 45th song. Original model. 1810.

457 — Hymen. Nysø 1843. Cast.

497 — Ulysses receiving Achilles' Weapons, awarded him by Minerva, whilst Ajax departs in Despair. In the middle, Achilles' tomb on which is seated his Mother, the Sea-Goddess Thetis. 1831. Marble.

ROOM X

The theme of the ceiling decoration is taken from the House of the Laby-rinth in Pompeii. The composition is the work of C. Løffler who has personally painted the six herms. A number of artists, including C. F. Sørensen, are responsible for the rest of the ceiling.

4   STATUE. Mercury about to slay Argus. 1818. Marble (Thorvaldsen). Purchased in London, 1938.

325   RELIEF. Minerva. Original model. C. 1836.

326   — Apollo. Original model. C. 1836.

352   — Pan teaching a little Satyr to blow a reed-pipe. 1831. Marble.

354   — Bacchante holding up a bunch of Grapes for a little Satyr. 1833. Marble.

407   — Cupid with Bacchus. Marble. Remodelling of No. 409A in Room IV.

416   — Cupid received by Anacreon. Marble. Remodelling of No. 414 in Room IV.

ROOM XI

The ceiling decoration is designed by the architect, W. Henck and executed by G. C. Hilker and William Klein (the ornaments). The theme is from Hadrian's Villa.

166 STATUE. Countess Ostermann. 1815. Marble (H. V. Bissen). The original marble work is in the Hermitage, Leningrad.

171   — Princess Maria Feodorowna Bariatinsky. 1818. Marble (Thorvaldsen).

239   BUST. Countess Giovanna Nugent. Original model. Presumably modelled in 1818.

278   — Marchesa Marianna Florenzi. Original model. 1828.

306 BUST. Portrait of a Lady. Original model.

A893 — Thomson Henry Bonar. 1817. Marble (Thorvaldsen). Purchased 1950.

451 RELIEF. Cupid and Hymen. Nysø 1840. Marble (H. V. Bissen).

553 — Rebecca and Eliezer at the Well. Original model. Nysø 1840-41.

618A — Baron Schubart bidding Farewell to his dying Wife. 1814. Memorial to Baroness Jacoba Elisabeth Schubart. Marble (Thorvaldsen).

ROOM XII

The theme of the ceiling decoration is from the Tepidarium in the old baths at Pompeii. The figures are executed by G. Chr. Freund, the stucco friezes and ornaments by C. Weber, William Klein and C. F. Sørensen. The chief picture in the centre, the lunettes, etc. are the work of G. C. Hilker.

124 EQUESTRIAN STATUE. Prince Jozef Poniatowski. Preliminary to the colossal statue in the Entrance Gallery. Partly an original model. 1822-23.

203 BUST. Christian, Duke of Augustenburg. 1819. Marble (Thorvaldsen).

207 — Portrait of Man. Marble (Thorvaldsen).

221 — Fr. Siegfried Vogt, Danish Diplomatist, Chargé d'affaires in Naples. 1837. Marble.

229 — J. C. Dahl, Norwegian landscape painter. Original model. 1821.

234 — Prince Clemens Metternich. 1819. Marble (Thorvaldsen).

236 — General, Prince Karl Philipp von Schwarzenberg, Duke of Krumau. Original model. 1821.

241   BUST. Henri François Brandt, Swiss Medallist. Original model. Presumably modelled in 1817.

242   — C. H. Donner, German Merchant. Original model. Copenhagen 1840.

246   — The Emperor Alexander I. Modelled in Warsaw 1820. Marble (Thorvaldsen). Purchased 1946.

257   — Lord Byron, the Poet. Original model. 1817.

263   — Edward Divett, Esquire of Bystock, Devon. Original model. 1817.

272   — Count G. B. Sommariva. C. 1817-18. Marble.

289   — Sir George Hilaro Barlow, Governor General of India. 1828. Marble (Thorvaldsen). Presented to the Museum in 1950, by Victoria, Lady Barlow, Thruxton, Andover.

290   — Portrait of a Man. Original model.

316   RELIEF. Jupiter enthroned between Minerva and Nemesis; below, the God of the Sea and the Goddess of the Earth. This is the original model for the frontispiece relief on the front of the former Christiansborg Palace in Copenhagen which was built by C. F. Hansen. 1808.

422   — Cupid upon a Swan. Original model. Nysø 1840.

614   — Monument to Auguste Böhmer. The departed is handing her sick mother a potion. On the sides, Nemesis and the Genius of Death. Original models. C. 1812.

615   — Monument to Philip Bethmann-Hollweg, who died in Florence immediately before his brother arrived in order to present him with a reward from the Emperor of Austria for noble services rendered. This is symbolized in the centre relief. On the left-hand relief, Philip's sorrowing mother and sisters; on the right, the Goddess of Justice, Nemesis, re-

cords Philip's noble deed. The place of death, Florence, is symbolized by the deity of the River Arno. In marble, in the sepulchral chapel of the von Bethmanns and the Bethmann-Hollwegs in the main cemetery, Frankfort-on-the-Main. Original model. 1814.

619 RELIEF. Monument to Countess Anna Maria Porro Serbelloni. The sorrowing husband and children of the departed. In marble, in the Galleria d'Arte Moderna, Milan. Original model. 1817.

ROOM XIII

The centre panel of the ceiling decoration depicts a scene from an antique play and is executed by Magnus Petersen from a copy by Chr. Købke. With J. P. Rasmussen and J. J. G. Guntzelnick the first-mentioned has executed the detail drawings and the ornaments from themes taken from Roman mosaics.

121 STATUE. Couching Lion. 1825. Marble (Thorvaldsen).

130 — Lord Byron, the poet. Original model. 1831. Executed in marble from the altered model No. 132 (page 63) and erected in Trinity College, Cambridge.

210 BUST. Henrik Hielmstierne, Danish Collector of Books. Original model. Presumably 1812.

260 — Admiral Edward Pellew, later Viscount Exmouth. Original model. 1814.

278 A — Marchesa Marianna Florenzi. 1828. Marble (H. V. Bissen).

131 RELIEF. The Genius of Poetry. In marble on Lord Byron's monument in Trinity College, Cambridge. 1831. Marble.

343 RELIEF. Cupid listening to the song of Erato. 1830. Marble.

357-58 — A Satyr dancing with a Bacchante. Original models. Nysø 1841 and 1843.

365 — The Fates with the Thread of Life. 1833. Marble (H. V. Bissen).

614A — Monument to Auguste Böhmer. C. 1812. Marble (Thorvaldsen).

ROOM XIV

The ceiling is decorated by A. F. Behrends, Th. Wegener and
W. Hammer after a theme from the burial chamber in
the Cestius Pyramid.

44 STATUE. Ganymede with the Eagle of Jupiter. 1817. Marble (Thorvaldsen).

347A RELIEF. Mercury bringing the Infant Bacchus to Ino. 1809. Marble (Th. Stein).

351 — Hebe presenting Ganymede with a Pitcher and a Bowl. Original model. 1833.

389 — Cupid upon the Lion. 1831. Marble.

391 — Cupid writing down the Laws of Jupiter. 1831. Marble (Thorvaldsen).

417 — Cupid complaining to Venus of a Bee-sting. From Anacreon's 40th song. 1809. Marble (Thorvaldsen).

424 — Shepherdess with a Cupid's Nest. 1831. Marble (Thorvaldsen).

484 — Hylas being abducted by the River Nymphs. 1833. Marble (Thorvaldsen).

ROOM XV

The ceiling decoration is designed by W. Hammer and for the most part executed by him with the aid of Th. Wegener, Herman Hjernøe and A. F. Behrends. The theme is taken from Nero's Golden House (formerly called Titus' Baths).

155A STATUE. Count Wlodzimierz Potočki. The original marble work was executed for the tomb of the Count in the cathedral on Wawell hill, Cracow. 1821. Marble (C. Peters).

248 BUST. Princess Maria Alekseevna Narischkin. Original model.

291 — Count Arthur Potočki. 1829. Original model.

359 RELIEF. Victory recording Exploits on a Shield. C. 1830. Marble.

362 — Victory standing with a Shield and a Palm Branch. Original model. C. 1830. Like No. 359, originally intended for the Potočki statue (see No. 155A).

364 — Nemesis in a Biga, followed by the Genii of Punishment and Reward. Original model. 1834. Executed in marble for the memorial to Julius Mylius at the Villa Vigoni, Lake Como.

514 — Thaïs luring Alexander to set Persepolis on fire. 1832. Marble (H. V. Bissen).

ROOM XVI

The genii in the ceiling rosettes as well as the Dance of the Muses on Helicon, in the lunette on the back wall, have been executed by J. F. Busch and N. Borggreen from Thorvaldsen's own composition. The remaining decorations are by W. Hammer and Herman Hjernøe.

22A STATUE. The Triumphant Cupid examining the Point of his Arrow. 1814. Marble (Th. Stein).

377-80. RELIEFS. Cupid holding Sway over the World. 377, Cupid in Heaven on Jupiter's Eagle, with the Thunderbolt. 378, Cupid on Earth as the Tamer of the Lion, with Hercules' Club. 379, Cupid on the Sea on the back of a Dolphin, with Neptune's Trident. 380, Cupid in the Underworld as the Conqueror of Cerebus, with a Fire-Fork. Also described as: The Four Elements. Modelled 1828. Marble.

395   RELIEF. Cupid and Ganymede throwing Dice. The theme is from a poem by Simonides. 1831. Marble (Thorvaldsen).

454   — Cupid and Hymen spinning the Thread of Life. 1831. Marble.

ROOM XVII

The ceiling is decorated by C. Weber, G. Chr. Freund, Joel Ballin, David Jacobsen and Ludv. Lehmann. The theme is from Diomedes' Villa in Pompeii.

53 A STATUE. Adonis. 1808. Marble (C. Peters).

218 A BUST. Ida Brun, Countess de Bombelles, Danish mime dancer. 1810. Marble (Thorvaldsen). Bequeathed to the Museum by Fr. Brun, Chamberlain at the Danish court, in 1902.

235   — Prince Clemens Metternich. Original model. 1819.

245 A — Karoline von Rehfues. 1827. Marble (Thorvaldsen). Purchased 1923.

259   — Lord George Granville Leveson Gower, later Duke of Sutherland. Original model. 1921.

480   RELIEF. The Centaur Nessus embracing the reluctant Deianira. 1814. Marble (Thorvaldsen).

488A RELIEF. The Centaur Chiron teaching Achilles to throw the Spear. 1837. Marble (Th. Stein).

646A — Hunter, on Horseback. 1834. Marble (C. Peters).

647A — Huntress, on Horseback. 1834. Marble (C. Peters).

ROOM XVIII

The centre-panel of the ceiling decoration depicting the Times of the Day, has been painted by Th. Wegener; the moss garlands are the work of W. Hammer, whilst N. Borggreen and J. F. Busch are responsible for the ornaments.

31 GROUP. The Graces with Cupid's Arrow, and Cupid playing the Lyre. Remodelling of the group in Room III. 1842. Marble (H. V. Bissen).

191A BUST. King Frederik VI. Copenhagen, 1819. Marble (Thorvaldsen). 1923.

192A — Queen Marie Sophie Frederikke. Copenhagen 1819. Marble (Thorvaldsen). Purchased 1923.

193A — Princess Caroline. Daughter of Frederik VI. Copenhagen 1819. Marble (Thorvaldsen). Purchased 1922.

195 — Princess Vilhelmine Marie, Daughter of Frederik VI. Presumably modelled in 1828. Marble (Thorvaldsen).

279 — Vittoria Caldoni of Albano. 1821. Marble(Thorvaldsen). Purchased 1947.

307 — Jane Craufurd. Original model. 1818.

328-333. RELIEFS. The muses. 328, Clio. 329, Euterpe. 330, Thalia. 331, Melpomene. 332, Terpsichore. 333, Erato. 334, Polyhymnia. 335, Urania. 336, Calliope. Original models. C. 1836.

337 RELIEF. The Mother of the Muses, Mnemosyne, with Harpocrates. Original model. C. 1836.

4*

525   RELIEF. The Genii of the Three Creative Arts (Paint-
        ing, Architecture, Sculpture). Original model.
        Nysø 1843.

ROOM XIX

*The figures in the ceiling decoration, the Graces and the ornaments in
the coffers are the work of David Jacobsen and Ludvig Lehmann; the
remaining decorations are executed by Ph. Aug. Fischer.*

176A STATUE. Shepherd Boy. 1817. Marble (Thorvaldsen).
        Purchased 1952. A marble replica is to be found
        in the Hermitage, Leningrad.

406   RELIEF. Cupid offering a Rose whilst hiding the
        Thistles. Original model. 1837.

421   — Cupid riding upon a Swan. Original model. Nysø
        1840.

482   — Hylas being abducted by the River Nymphs. 1831.
        Marble.

638-641. RELIEFS. The Ages of Life and The Seasons of the
        Year. 638, Childhood - Spring .639, Youth -
        Summer. 640, Manhood - Autumn. 641, Old Age
        –Winter. Modelled 1836. Marble.

ROOM XX

*The ceiling decorations is the work of C. F. Sørensen, C. Weber, G. Chr.
Freund, W. Klein and Joel Ballin. The latter is also responsible for the
perspective picture on the gable.*

162A STATUE. Thorvaldsen leaning on his statue of "Hope".
        Modelled at Nysø 1839. Marble (H. V. Bissen).

197   BUST. King Christian VIII as Successor to the Throne.
        Original model. 1921. Included in the Museum
        1854.

198 BUST. Queen Caroline Amalie as Princess. 1820. Cast. Included in the Museum 1854.

199 — King Frederik VII when a young Prince. Original model. Copenhagen, 1820.

200 — The above at a later age. 1828. Marble.

232 — King Ludwig I of Bavaria as Crown Prince. 1818. Marble (Thorvaldsen).

281 — Vincenzo Camuccini, Italian painter. 1810. Marble (Thorvaldsen).

342 RELIEF. The muses of Tragedy and Comedy. Original model. Nysø 1843.

518A — Art and the light-bringing Genius. "A genio lumen". 1808. Marble (Thorvaldsen). Presented by Thorvaldsen to Thomas Hope 1828. Purchased in England, 1917.

528 — The Genii of Poetry and Harmony. Original model. Nysø 1843.

601 — The Graces listening to the song of Cupid. In marble on the monument to the painter Appiani in the Brera collection, Milan. 1821. Marble.

ROOM XXI

The ceiling is composed over a theme from Nero's Golden House (formerly called Titus' Baths). Jørgen Sonne has painted the Madonna and Child, eight angels, seven panels with animals, four panels with biblical motifs, and the four Evangelists. Th. Wegener has executed the Flight to Egypt, the Slaughter of the Innocents at Bethlehem and four hovering angels. A. F. Behrends, W. Hammer and E. Fich have painted the white angels and the ornaments on the blue ground.

150 STATUE. Conradin, the last of the Hohenstaufen Emperors. Original model. 1836. Erected in marble in the Church of Sta. Maria del Carmine, Naples.

152   STATUE. King Christian IV. Original model. Copen-
      hagen 1840. The original bronze work (cast and
      chased by J. B. Dalhoff) is in King Christian IV's
      Chapel, Roskilde Cathedral.

164   — Queen Caroline Amalie as Princess. Original mo-
      del. 1827.

191   BUST. King Frederik VI. Copenhagen 1819. Cast.

192   — Queen Marie Sophie Frederikke. Original model.
      Copenhagen 1819.

193   — Princess Caroline, Daughter of Frederik VI.
      Original model. Copenhagen 1819.

196   — Princess Vilhelmine Marie, Daughter of Frederik
      VI. Original model. Presumably modelled in 1828.

201   — Prince Friedrich Wilhelm of Hessen-Philippsthal,
      Danish Officer. 1822. Cast.

202   — Princess Juliane Sophie. Consort of the above,
      Daughter of Prince Frederik, the Heir Presumptive.
      1822. Cast.

557   RELIEF. The Baptism of Christ. Copenhagen 1820.
      Cast. In marble in the Church of Our Lady, Co-
      penhagen.

558   — The Institution of the Lord's Supper. Copenhagen
      1820. Cast. In marble in the Church of Our Lady,
      Copenhagen.

563   — Christ with the two Disciples at Emaus. Nysø
      1839. Modelled for the altar-piece in Stavreby
      (Jungshoved) Church, near Præstø. Cast. Purchased
      1845.

599   — Christian Charity, with Faith and Hope. Original
      model. 1836.

                    *   *   *

FIRST FLOOR

THORVALDSEN'S WORKS AND HIS COLLECTIONS OF
PAINTINGS, DRAWINGS, ANTIQUES, BOOKS, ETC.

STAIRCASE

*The ceiling decoration in the vestibule is designed and painted by J. Chr.
Larsen. The figures in the well of the staircase are executed by Joel Ballin,
and the ornaments by H. C. Nickelsen. The theme is from the House of
the Labyrinth, Pompeii (see Room X).*

14 STATUE. Hercules. Copenhagen 1843. Original model.
In bronze in Prince Jørgen's Gaard (the courtyard
of Christiansborg Palace).

308 BUST. Portrait of a Lady. Original model.

312A — Wilhelmine, Duchess of Sagan. Modelled in 1819.
Cast, made before the locks of hair on the forehead and on the temples were added (see No. 312,
page 57). Presented by Baron August Binzer,
Munich, in 1909.

398 RELIEF. Cupid caressing the faithful Dog. Original
model. 1831.

399 — Cupid making a Butterfly-net, symbolizing the
Soul, or the fleeting Heart. Original model. 1831.

450 — Cupid and Psyche. Original model. Nysø 1840.

452 — Cupid and Hymen. Original model. Nysø 1840.

456 — Cupid's Swan Song. Original model. Nysø 1843.

481 — Nessus, the Centaur, embracing the protesting
Deianira. Original model. 1814.

488 — Chiron, the Centaur, teaching Achilles to throw
the Spear. Original model. 1837.

520 RELIEF. The Genius of Painting. Original model. Nysø 1843.

521 — The Genius of Architecture. Original model. Nysø 1843.

522-23 RELIEFS. The Genius of Sculpture. Original model. Nysø 1843.

527 RELIEF. The Genius of Poetry. Original model. Copenhagen 1844.

646 — Hunter on Horseback. Original model. 1834.

647 — Huntress on Horseback. Original model. 1834.

*

The synchronous pillar on the landing, first floor, gives a simultaneous view of Thorvaldsen's life, his work and his times in facts and figures.

The pillar is divided into narrow, vertical panels, each representing one year. As you revolve the pillar you will see the time of Thorvaldsen and its events in progressive series.

The long *bands* at the top indicate the most important dates in the life of Thorvaldsen and his next-of-kin, as well as his sojourn in Denmark and Italy. Next follow the *yellow* labels with details of Thorvaldsen's life, *photographs* of his works, *green* labels which indicate outstanding cultural events, *blue* labels with historical and political events whilst, below, the *grey* labels record the dates of the births and deaths of famous characters. The *blue* band at the bottom shows what Danish kings reigned in Thorvaldsen's lifetime.

(The synchronous pillar was devised and made by the Danish artist, *Poul Sæbye*).

CORRIDOR

The theme for the ceiling decoration is taken from Nero's Golden House (formerly called Titus' Baths). The execution is the joint work of Heinrich Hansen, C. F. Sørensen, A. P. Madsen, W. Hammer, William Klein, N. Borggreen, C. Weber, Chr. Løffler, E. Fich, M. M. Goldschmidt and J. J. G. Guntzelnick. J. F. Busch, J. P. Rasmussen, F. C. Lund, Ph. Aug. Fischer and A. F. Behrends are also said to have participated.

STATUES

2 Bacchus. Original model. 1804.

3 Apollo. Original model. 1805.

12 Venus with the Apple. Original model. 1813-16.

22 Cupid Triumphant. 1814. Cast.

24 Cupid Triumphant. 1823. Cast.

26 Psyche with the Beauty Ointment. Original model. 1806.

28 Cupid and Psyche re-united in Heaven. Cupid, a cast. Psyche, an original model. 1807.

32 The Graces and Cupid. 1842. Cast. Remodelling of No. 29 in Room III.

34 Cupid, seated, with the Lyre. Original model. 1819. Gift from Thorvaldsen to C. Voigt, the German medallist. Purchased 1882.

36 Cupid, standing, with his Bow. Cast.

37 Hebe. Original model. 1806.

39A Hebe. 1816. Remodelling of No. 37. Perhaps an original model. Purchased 1934.

41 Ganymede offering the brimming Bowl. 1804. Cast.

43 Ganymede filling the Drinking Bowl. 1816. Cast.

45 Ganymede with Jupiter's Eagle. 1817. Cast.

47 The Goddess of Hope. Original model. 1817.

132 Lord Byron. 1831. The head is a cast of the bust,

No. 257, in Room XII, the remainder is a cast of the original model in Room XIII. Executed in marble for Trinity College, Cambridge.

167   Countess Ostermann. Original model. 1815.

172   Princess Bariatinsky. Original model. 1818.

173   Georgiana Elizabeth Russell. 1814-15. Cast.

174   A young girl (Jeanina Stampe), as Psyche. Original model. Nysø 1840.

177   Shepherd Boy. Original model. 1817.

178   A Dancing Girl. Original model. 1817.

179   A Dancing Girl. Cast. Remodelling of No. 178. Executed in marble for Torlonia in Rome.

181   Young Girl dancing. Original model. 1837.

BUSTS

190   Ludvig Holberg, Danish comedy writer. Nysø 1839. Original model.

213   Baron, Admiral Hans Holsten. Original model. Modelled in Copenhagen or at Nysø, in 1840.

215   Countess Henriette Danneskiold-Samsøe. Original model. Nysø 1839.

217   Baroness Christine Stampe. Rome 1842. Cast.

218   Ida Brun, Countess de Bombelles, Danish mime dancer. Original model. 1810.

222   Fr. Siegfried Vogt, Danish Diplomatist, Chargé d'affaires in Naples. Original model. 1837.

226   Adam Oehlenschlæger, Danish Poet. Original model. Nysø 1839.

227   Caspar Bartholin, Graduate in Law. A marble copy was made in 1824, the model having been made at an earlier date.

230   Jørgen Knudtzon, Merchant of Trondheim, Norway. Original model. 1816.

231 H. C. Knudtzon, Merchant of Trondheim, Norway. Original model. 1816.

238 Countess Alexandrine von Dietrichstein. Original model. Presumably modelled between 1810-1815.

243 Baron A. E. von Eichthal, Banker to the Bavarian Court. Original model. 1831.

250 Princess Maria Feodorowna Bariatinsky, Consort of Prince I. Bariatinsky. Original model. 1818.

251 Countess Anna Potočka. Original model.

262 Alexander Baillie. Original model. 1816.

264A Louisa Hope, wife of Thomas Hope. Presumably modelled in the winter of 1816-17. Marble (Thorvaldsen). Bought at the Hope sale in England 1917.

269 Countess Julie Potočka. Original model. 1833.

274 Count G. B. Sommariva. Original model. Presumably modelled C. 1822-23.

277 Giovanni Raimondo Torlonia, Duke of Bracciano, a Rome banker. 1829. Cast

293 Prince Nicolaus Esterházy. Original model. 1817.

294 Henry Labouchère, later Lord Taunton, English Statesman. Original model. 1828.

298 Thomas Hope. Presumably modelled in the winter of 1816-17. Marble (Thorvaldsen). Bought at the Hope sale in England 1917.

299 George Agar Ellis, later Baron Dover. Original model. 1818.

300 Count François Gabriel de Bray. Original model. Winter 1818-19.

309 Lady Harriet Frances Fleetwood Pellew. Original model. 1817.

312 Wilhelmine, Duchess of Sagan. Original model, with locks of hair on the forehead and the temples added later. 1819. (See No. 312A, page 53).

292   296-297. 310-11 and 313. Unidentified Portraits. All original models.

674   Portrait of a Man. Marble (Thorvaldsen).

RELIEFS

134   The Genius of Poetry. Original model. 1831. Modelled for Byron's statue. (See No. 131, Room XIII).

339   Procession to Parnassus. Apollo with Pegasus and the Genius of Light; the Graces and the Muses, accompanied by cupids; Homer, led by the Genius of Poetry. Original model. 1832.

341   The Dance of the Muses on Helicon. Modelled at the Villa Montenero, near Leghorn in 1804, remodelled in 1816. Original model.

347   Mercury bringing the Infant Bacchus to Ino. Original model. 1809.

353   Pan and a little Satyr. Original model. 1831.

355   A Bacchante and a little Satyr. Original model. 1833.

356   A lustful Pan and a Hunting Nymph. Original model. C. 1838.

356A A lustful Pan and a Hunting Nymph. C. 1838. Marble (Thorvaldsen).

360   Victory. Original model. C. 1830. Modelled for the pedestal of Napoleon's bust, but not used.

369   Night. Original model. 1815.

370   Day. Original model. 1815.

372   Cupid feeding Hygeia's Serpent. Original model. 1837.

376   Cupid, in Fetters, with the Graces. Original model. 1831.

381-384. Cupid holding Sway over the World, or The Four Elements. 381, Cupid i Heaven on Jupiter's Eagle, with the Thunderbolt. 382, Cupid on Earth as the Tamer

of the Lion, with Hercules' Club. 383, Cupid on the
Sea on the back of a Dolphin, with Neptune's Trident.
384, Cupid in the Underworld as Cerberus' conqueror,
with a Fire-fork. Original models. 1828.

385-386 Cupid upon Jupiter's Eagle. Original models.

387 Cupid with the tamed Lion. Original model.

387A Cupid with the tamed Lion. Marble.

390 Cupid upon the Lion. 1831. Cast.

392 Cupid writing down Jupiter's Laws. Original model.
1831.

394 Cupid pleading with Jupiter to make the Rose the
Queen o Flowers. Original model. 1831.

400 Cupid sailing. Original model. 1831.

404 Cupid setting the Rock on Fire. Original model. 1831.

408 Cupid with Bacchus. Original model. 1810.

411 Cupid with a Swan, and Boys plucking Fruit –
Summer. Original model. Montenero. 1810.

413 Cupid and the young Bacchus trampling Grapes
under Foot – Autumn. From Anacreon's 17th song.
Original model. Montenero. 1810.

415 Cupid being received by Anacreon – Winter. From
Anacreon's 3rd song. 1823. Cast.

417A Cupid complaining to Venus of a Bee-sting. Original
model. 1809. Presented by the sculptor. G. Chr.
Freund, 1876.

431 Cupid reviving the fainting Psyche. Original model.
Montenero, 1810.

433-448 Representations of the Myth: Cupid and Psyche.
Modelled 1838 from Thorvaldsen's drawings by
Pietro Galli for the Palazzo Torlonia, Rome, now
demolished. Casts.

455 Cupid and Hymen spinning the Thread of Life.
Original model. 1831.

458-479 Various mythological scenes. 458, The fleeing Latona. 459, Diana with her Hind. 460-461, Diana and Actaeon. 461 A, Actaeon. 462-463, Diana and Orion. 464, Chione and Daedalion. 465-466, Diana and Endymion. 467-471, The Nymphs of Diana. 472, Callisto. 473, Atalanta. 474, Meleager. 475, A Hero with a slain Lion. 476, Adonis. 477, Narcissus. 478, Apollo and Daphne. 479, Pan with the Syrinx, the Pan pipe. Modelled 1837 from Thorvaldsen's drawings by Pietro Galli for the Palazzo Torlonia, Rome, now demolished. Casts. (No. 461 A: Presented by the sculptor, G. Chr. Freund, in 1875).

483 Hylas being abducted by the River Nymphs. Original model. 1831.

485 Hylas being abducted by the River Nymphs. Original model. 1833.

490 Briseïs being led away from Achilles by the Heralds of Agamennon. The first relief executed by Thorvaldsen Rome. Original model. 1803.

492 Priam supplicating Achilles for Hector's Body. Original model. 1815.

494 Achilles bandaging the wounds of Patroclus. Original model. 1837.

496 Achilles with the slain Amazon Penthesilea. Original model. 1837.

498 Ulysses receiving Achilles' Weapons, awarded him by Minerva, whilst Ajax departs in Despair. Original model. 1831.

499 Hector with Paris and Helen. 1809. Cast.

501 Hector saying Farewell to Andromache. Original model. 1837.

508 FRIEZE. Alexander's Procession, reduced scale. Executed in marble by Pietro Galli in 1822 and following years.

509 Variant of the centre-piece of the foregoing frieze. Marble.

510-511 Parts of the original models for the Alexander Procession. The Market Place by the River. A Mother and her Children with the Sheeps.

512 An addition to the Alexander Procession. A Youth leading a Horse. Original model. 1829.

513 An addition to the Alexander Procession. A Warrior leading a Horse. Original model. 1831.

515 Thaïs luring Alexander to set Persepolis on fire. Original model. 1832. (See No. 516, page 32).

518 Art and the light-bringing Genius. "A genio lumen". Original model. 1808.

532-545 The Genii of: 532, Poetry. 533, Tragedy. 534, Comedy. 535, Music. 536, Dancing. 537, Government. 538, War. 539, Navigation. 540, Trade. 541, Medicine. 542, Horticulture. 543, Agriculture. 544, Astronomy. 545, Religion. Modelled in 1838 from Thorvaldsen's drawings by Pietro Galli for the Palazzo Torlonia in Rome, now demolished. Casts.

549 Justice. Original model. Nysø 1841.

556 Mary with the Infant Jesus and St. John. Original model. 1806.

562 Christ and the two Disciples at Emaus. Original model 1818. Executed in silver for the ciborium on the high altar of the Church of SS. Annunziata, Florence.

565 Christ entrusting the Government of the Church to St. Peter. Original model. 1818. In marble on the front of the communion table in the Palace Chapel of Villa Poggio Imperiale, near Florence.

571 Mary's Flight from the Slaughter of the Innocents at Bethlehem. Original model. 1832.

579-582 The four Evangelists. Original models. 1833.

586   Angels, singing. Original model. 1833.

588   Angels, playing instruments. Original model. 1833.

590-592.   Angels with Flowers and Garlands. Executed in bronze for the High Altar in the Cathedral of Novara. Original models. 1833.

602   The Graces listening to Cupid's song. On the memorial to the painter Appiani in the Brera Collection, Milan. 1821. Cast.

626   The Genius of Death. Executed for Prince W. Potočki's tomb. 1829. Marble.

628   Praying Children. Executed for Count Arthur Potočki's tomb in the Cracow Cathedral. Original model. 1834.

629   PORTRAIT MEDALLION. Andrea Appiani, Italian Painter. Original model. Presumably modelled in 1821.

631   — Carlo (Charles) Bassi, Architect. 1797-98. Cast.

632   — August von Goethe (Son of the Poet). Original model. 1831. In marble on the memorial to A. v. G., in the Protestant cemetery in Rome.

633   — Henrich Steffens, Philosopher. Original model. Nysø 1840.

635   — Portrait of a Lady. Original model.

636   Thorvaldsen with the Family Stampe. From left to right Christian, Thorvaldsen, Jeanina, Baroness Stampe, and Elise. Nysø 1840. Cast.

637   Baron Stampe and his sons, Henrik (the hunter) and Holger (the rider). Nysø 1840. Cast.

642-645   The Ages of Life and the Seasons of the Year. 642, Childhood - Spring. 643, Youth - Summer. 644, Manhood - Autumn. 645, Old Age - Winter. Original models. 1836.

ROOM XXII

The coffers of the ceiling, with themes from Roman mosaics, are designed by E. Fich and executed by himself in co-operation with William Klein and J. J. G. Guntzelnick.

194   BUST. Princess Vilhelmine Marie. Original model. Copenhagen, 1819.

261   — Lord William Bentinck, later governor general of India. Original model. 1816.

265   — Henry Hope, eldest son of Thomas Hope. Original model. Presumably modelled 1821.

266   — Younger son of Thomas Hope. Presumably modelled in the winter 1816-17. Cast.

405   RELIEF. Cupid offering a Rose whilst hiding the Thistles. Original model. 1837.

PAINTINGS

66   *Ippolito Caffi.* Festive Evening in Venice.

172   *Karl Markó.* Italian Mountain Landscape. 1836.

173   — Italian Mountain Landscape. 1836.

176   *C. G. Plagemann.* A Nun in her Cell.

178   *J. C. Dahl.* The Bay of Naples by Moonlight. 1821.

179   — Vesuvius in Eruption: Moonlight. 1821.

180   — Grotto in the Bay of Naples: Moonlight. 1821.

181   — The Piazza of St. Peter's by Moonlight. 1821.

182   — Highway, La Storta, Italy. 1821.

183   — A Waterfall, Italy. 1821.

184   — Norwegian Mountain Landscape and Cataract. 1821.

185   — Jordalsnuten, Norway. 1821.

186   — Norwegian Mountain Valley. 1821.

187   — Entrance to Copenhagen Harbour. 1830.

192   *Thomas Fearnley.* Capri viewed from Sorrento. 1833.

5

ROOM XXIII

The ceiling decoration is executed by E. Fich and William Klein; the theme is from Nero's Golden House (formerly called Titus' Baths).

373   RELIEF. Hygeia being wreathed by Cupid. Original model. Nysø 1840.

PAINTINGS

61   *G. B. Bassi*. Road between Villas and Garden Walls (Terni). 1820.

63   — Scene from the Ruins of the Imperial Palaces, Rome.

67   *Vincenzo Camuccini*. Christ blessing little Children.

78   *L. Fioroni*. Festive Evening in a Roman Osteria. 1830.

79   — Pope Pius VIII being carried in Procession.

82   *T. Gazzarini*. The Infant Jesus. 1822.

86   *M. Pacetti*. The Posilip Grotto, near Naples. Copy after G. B. Bassi.

87   *P. Chauvin*. Scene from the Garden of the Villa Falconieri in Frascati. 1810.

88   — Scene from the Garden of the Villa d'Este in Tivoli. 1811.

89   — Grotta ferrata near the Alban Hills. 1811.

91   *Tancrède de la Bouère*. Coast Scene near the Pontine Marshes. 1838.

92   *Leopold Robert*. The Church of San Paolo fuori le mura on the day after the fire of 1823. 1825.

93   — A young Greek sharpening his Dagger. 1829.

ROOM XXIV

The ceiling decoration is executed by Ludvig Lehmann, J. J. G. Cuntzel-nick and Chr. Løffler and contains themes from Diomedes' Villa, Pompeii.

23   STATUE. Cupid triumphant, examining his Arrow. 1823. Marble (H. V. Bissen).

214   BUST. Count Conrad Danneskiold-Samsøe, Danish Lord Lieutenant. Original model. Nordfeld. 1820.

216   — Countess Louise Danneskiold-Samsøe. Original model. Gisselfeld. 1820.

346   RELIEF. Mercury bringing the little Bacchus to Ino. Original model. 1809.

PAINTINGS

60   *G. B. Bassi.* View of a Glade from across a Brook. 1816.

62   — Woodland Path. 1824.

84   *G. Lazzarini.* The Roman Aqueduct, Aqua vergine. 1823.

94   *Horace Vernet.* Armenian Priest. 1830.

98   *Thomas Lawrence.* Cardinal Ercole Consalvi.

110   *F. Catel.* Grotto in Maecenas' Villa in Tivoli.

111   — Night Scene. Based on the final scene in René's Story, by Chateaubriand.

125   *J. A. Koch.* Apollo amongst the shepherds of Thessaly.

128   — View from the Interlaken Valley to the "Jungfrau", in the Bernese Oberland. The figures in the landscape are by *J. C. Dahl.* 1821.

139   *J. C. Reinhart.* Woodland Scene. 1793.

140   — Scene from the Garden of the Villa Borghese.

157   *G. Schick.* Heroic Landscape.

ROOM XXV

*The ceiling decoration is executed by C. F. Sørensen; the theme is from
Nero's Golden House (formerly called Titus' Baths).*

173A STATUE. Georgiana Elizabeth Russell. 1814-15.
   Marble (H. V. Bissen). In marble at Woburn
   Abbey.

401 RELIEF. Cupid sailing. Original model. 1831.

PAINTINGS

109 *F. Catel.* Neapolitan Fisher Family.

113 *P. Cornelius.* The Burial of Christ. 1815.

122 *A. Hopfgarten.* The Miracle of St. Elizabeth. 1832.

126 *J. A. Koch.* Italian Landscape.

127 — Italian Landscape. In middle distance: Olevano in
   the Sabine Mountains. (At the bottom right corner,
   the painter's self-portrait).

134 *E. F. Oehme.* Scene from a Gothic Church.

135 *M. Oppenheim.* The Homecoming of Tobias. 1823.

136 *J. F. Overbeck.* Mary with the Infant Jesus.

141 *J. C. Reinhart.* Scene from Ponte Lupo near Tivoli.
   1823.

143 — Italian Landscape. In the foreground, a hunter.
   1835.

145 *Heinrich Reinhold.* Landscape with the Good Samari-
   tan. 1823.

146 — Landscape with Hagar and Ishmael. 1823.

147 — St. Peter's Church from the Garden of the Villa
   Doria Pamfili. In the background, Soracte and
   the Sabine Mountains. 1823.

156 *F. W. Schadow.* Jesus on his Way to Calvary.

160 *J. H. Schilbach.* View of Forum from the Capitolium.
   1826.

166 *T. Weller*. Jugglers on the Piazza Montanara, Rome. 1829.

171 *Karl Markó*. Landscape with bathing Hunting Nymphs. 1834.

299 Copy after *A. J. Carstens*. The Golden Age. The figures are painted by *J. J. Rubbi,* the landscape by *F. Catel*.

ROOM XXVI

The ceiling decoration is executed by Magnus Petersen; the theme is from Nero's Golden House (formerly called Titus' Baths).

37A STATUE. Hebe. 1806. Marble (Thorvaldsen). Purchased in London, 1938.

264 BUST. Louisa Hope, wife of Thomas Hope. Original model. Presumably modelled in 1816-17.

228 — Mrs. Høyer, the Mother of C. F. Høyer, the painter. Original model. 1809.

345 RELIEF. Diana entreating Jupiter to allow her to follow the chase. Original model. Nysø 1840.

PAINTINGS

64 *Ippolito Caffi*. Moccoli Evening in Rome. 1834.

161 *A. Senff*. Antique terra-cotta Vase with Flowers. 1828.

209 *C. W. Eckersberg*. Sleeping Woman in antique Clothing. Alcyone's Nurse. Fragment of the painting "Alcyone's Dream". Ovid's Metamorphoses, XI Song, 410-748. Rome, 1813.

212 — Socrates expounding a Proposition to Alcibiades who sits naked on a chair before him. 1813-1816.

213 — Hector taking leave of Andromache. 1813.

220 *Constantin Hansen*. Scene from the Poseidon Temple near Paestum. 1843.

230 *J. L. Jensen.* Flowers. 1833.

231 — Fruits. 1833.

236 — White Lilies and Sprays of a Rosetree.

253 *J. Th. Lundbye.* Landscape near Arresø, overlooking
the Sand Dunes at Tisvilde, Zealand. 1838.

254 — View from Vinderød towards Høbjerg near Fre-
deriksværk, showing the Home of Lundbye's
Parents, Zealand. 1839.

255 — Ancient Barrow near Raklev, Refnæs, Zealand. 1839.

271 *Ernst Meyer.* The Courtyard of the Franciscan
Monastery at Amalfi.

278 *J. P. Møller.* The Town of Svendborg, Funen. 1844.

282 *Fr. Petzholdt.* Landscape near Ancient Veji. 1835.

315 *Jens Juel.* Miss Wilhelmine Bertouch, Lady-in-Wait-
ing. Pastel. Presented to Thorvaldsen in 1838 by
the painter, Miss Caspara Preetzmann.

ROOM XXVII

*The ceiling decoration is executed by A. P. Madsen; the theme is from
Nero's Golden House (formerly called Titus' Baths).*

33 STATUE. Cupid playing the Lyre. 1818. Marble (H. V.
Bissen).

338 RELIEF. The Graces, floating. (See No. 374, Room
IX). Original model. C. 1836.

PAINTINGS

197 *W. Bendz.* Evening Assembly of Artists at Finck's
Coffee-House in Munich. 1832.

215 *C. W. Eckersberg.* Mary with the Infant Jesus, enthroned upon Clouds. 1816.

237 *Jens Juel.* View of Little Belt from Hindsgavl, Funen.

No. 197. W. Bendz: Finck's Coffe-House.

1) Heinlein. 2) H. Kaufmann. 3) J. M. Haeselich. 4) K. Altmann.
5) H. Crola. 6) A. Borum. 7) Eduard Schleich. 8) Marr. 9) Philip Foltz.
10) Daniel Fohr. 11) Morgenstern. 12) Fearnly. 13) Wilhelm Kaulbach.
14) Bernhard Stange. 15) Anton Zwengauer. 16) C.Christensen. 17) Alex.
Bruchmann. 18. Fr. W. Voertel. 19) W.. Bendz. 20) Joseph Petzl.

238   — View of Little Belt from a Hill near Middelfart, Funen.

239   — Landscape from the Lake of Geneva. 1777-79.

242   *J. A. Krafft.* Carnival Merrymakers in a Street in Rome. 1828.

258   *Wilh. Marstrand.* Merrymakers outside the Walls of Rome one Evening in October. 1839.

259   *H. D. C. Martens.* The Hall of Antiques, Royal Academy of Fine Arts at Charlottenborg Palace, Copenhagen. 1824.

268   *Ernst Meyer.* A Fisherman of Capri.

269   — Neapolitan Fisherman in his Doorway.

270   — A Fisherman of Capri.

273   — Young Franciscan (half-length portrait).

280   *O. D. Ottesen.* Fruits. 1842.

290   *L. A. Smith.* The painter, Vilhelm Gertner in his Room.

292   *Jørgen Sonne.* Roman Rustics outside the Osteria, near Ponte Mammolo. 1835.

301   *J. L. Lund.* Woman's Head.

ROOM XXVIII

The ceiling decoration is executed by Chr. Løffler. The tent theme is from an exedra in Nero's Golden House (formerly called Titus' Baths).

301   BUST. Michael Coronini-Cronberg, Austrian Count. Original model. 1816.

302   — Portrait of a Boy. Original model.

555   Baptismal font. 1805-07. With the exception of the wreath, it was made, in marble, for the chapel of Brahetrolleborg, on the island of Funen. Later marble copies, with the wreath, are to be found in the Reykjavik Cathedral, Iceland (executed in 1827), as well as in the Holy Spirit Church, Copenhagen.

PAINTINGS

133   *F. Nerly*. Buffaloes hauling a Block of Marble.

150   *A. Riedel*. Neapolitan Fisher Family. 1833.

201   *Heinrich Buntzen*. Oaks by the Water. 1840.

228   *C. V. Jensen*. The Manor of Gisselfeld, Zealand. 1839.

232   *J. L. Jensen*. Flowers. 1834.

246   *A. Küchler*. Roman Parents buying a Hat for their small Son who is going to be an Abbate. 1840.

247   — A young Abbate being heard his Lessons by his Sister.

249   *G. E. Libert*. View of the Sound from Langelinie, Copenhagen. 1839.

256   *A. C. Lunde*. Frederiksberg Palace, Copenhagen, from a place near Ladegaardsvejen.

266   *Ernst Meyer*. A Public Letter-Writer in a Street in Rome, reading a Letter to a yountg Girl. 1829.

267   — The same, writing a Letter for the young girl.

276   *Adam Müller*. Christ and the Evangelists. 1842.

279 *Hermania Neergaard*. Flowers. 1842.
284 *F. Richardt*. Painter's Studio, Charlottenborg Palace, Copenhagen (Royal Academy of Fine Arts).
286 *M. Rørbye*. View of Athens, from the South West. Athens, 1836.
291 *Jørgen Sonne*. The Battlefield on the Morning after an Encounter. 1833.
298 *F. Thøming*. Waves breaking on the shore of Capri.

ROOM XXIX

The ceiling decoration, a theme from Nero's Golden House (formerly called Titus' Baths), is executed by Heinrich Hansen.

35 STATUE. Cupid standing with his Bow. Marble (Thorvaldsen). Bought at the auction of Carl Jacobsen, Ph.D., of the Carlsberg Brewery, Copenhagen, in 1914.

PAINTINGS

58   *A. Aquaroni*. Ponte Cestio. 1836.
68   *A. Castelli*. Landscape.
101 *Penry Williams*. Shepherd Boy and a young Girl in the Roman Campagna. 1842.
138 *J. Rebell*. The Isle of Capri. 1820.
162 *J. Steingrübel*. View of Florence. 1834.
177 *J. C. Dahl*. The Bay of Naples: Moonlight. 1821.
198 *C. D. Blunck*. Noah in the Ark. 1835.
202 *Henrich Buntzen*. The so-called Raphael's Villa in the Garden of the Villa Borghese. 1843.
219 *F. Nordahl Grove*. View from Baunbjerg near Horsens Fjord, Jutland. 1842.

233 *J. L. Jensen*. Still Life. 1835.

234 — Flowers. 1838.

243 *A. Küchler*. The Death of Corregio. 1834.

244 — A Family Scene by Lake Nemi. 1837.

263 *Anton Melbye*. A serene Morning on the Sea. 1840.

277 *J. P. Møller*. Svendborg Sound. 1843.

293 *Fr. Thøming*. A Danish Corvette.

296 — Scene from the Coast of Capri. 1829.

ROOM XXX

The ceiling decoration, a theme from Nero's Golden House
(formerly called Titus' Baths), is painted by C. Weber.

244 BUST. Mrs. von Krause, wife of Jacob von Krause, Austrian Consul General at St. Petersburgh. Original model. 1819.

282 — Vincenzo Camuccini, Italian painter. Original model. 1810.

314 — Portrait of a child. Cast.

315 — Presumably of Georgiana Elizabeth Russell, and possibly a preliminary study for the statue No. 173 (Corridor, 1st floor). Original model.

126 SKETCH FOR A STATUE. Prince Jozef Poniatowski. Original model.

PAINTINGS

 74 *F. Diofebi*. Entrance to the Villa Borghese. 1838.

100 *J. Severn*. Vintage Merrymaking. 1828.

104 *M. Verstappen*. Chapel by the Road between Albano and Ariccia.

119 *A. Henning*. The model. Fortunata.

120 *G. E. Hering*. Street in Smyrna. 1835.

151 *A. Riedel.* Bathing Girl. 1837.

164 *C. L. Tischbein.* Neapolitan Fisher Girl.

165 *E. Wächter.* Joseph Anton Koch, Painter.

170 *Karl Markó.* Nymphs of the Chase bathing. 1834.

190 *Thomas Fearnley.* Norwegian. Landscape. 1833.

208 *Dankvart Dreyer.* Coast Scene from Aarhus, Jutland. Exhibited 1839.

241 *F. T. Kloss.* Entrance to Copenhagen Harbour. 1838.

251 *J. L. Lund.* St. Anna teaching Mary to read. Rom. (1818).

ROOM XXXI

The ceiling decoration, a theme from Diomedes' Villa in Pompeii, is painted by A. J. C. Riise.

25 STATUE. Psyche with the Beauty Ointment. 1806. Marble (Thorvaldsen). Bought at the Hope sale in England. 1917.

432 RELIEF. Mercury carrying Psyche to Heaven. Original model.

PAINTINGS

65 *Ippolito Caffi.* La Girandola at the Easter Celebration in Rome.

72 *F. Diofebi.* San Giuseppe Day in Rome. 1832.

73 — Opening of Raphael's Tomb in 1833 on which occasion Thorvaldsen represented the San Luca Academy in Rome. 1836.

80 *Beniamino de Francesco.* Italian Landscape. 1836.

95 *Horace Vernet.* Thorvaldsen. 1835.

105A *Friedrich von Amerling.* Thorvaldsen. (C. 1841-42). Purchased 1929.

148 *J. Richter.* The model, Fortunata. 1833.

No. 199. Blunck: Danish Artists in the La Gensola Osteria.
1) Küchler. 2) The Waiter. 3) Bindesbøll. 4) Marstrand. 5) Constantin Hansen. 6) Jørgen Sonne. 7) Blunck. 8) Ernst Meyer. 9) Thorvaldsen.

149   *J. Richter.* Roman Woman. 1834.

163 A *R. Suhrlandt.* Thorvaldsen. 1810. Presented to the Museum in 1921 by the family of the publisher, Oscar Gad.

164 A *Vogel von Vogelstein.* Thorvaldsen. 1814. Purchased 1890.

199   *D. C. Blunck.* Danish Artists in the La Gensola Osteria in Rome. 1837.

217   *C. W. Eckersberg.* The Arrival of Thorvaldsen at the Roads of Copenhagen, September 17, 1838. 1839.

258 C *Wilh. Marstrand.* M. G. Bindesbøll, Architect of Thorvaldsen's Museum. 1844. Loan from the Royal Gallery of Fine Arts, Copenhagen, in 1935; a bequest from Miss Johanne Bindesbøll.

281   *O. D. Ottesen.* A Luncheon Table. 1844.

285   *F. Richardt.* Thorvaldsen in his Studio in Charlottenborg Palace, Copenhagen. 1840.

287 *M. Rørbye.* Outdoor Scene at the Harbour of Palermo. 1844.
295 *Fr. Thøming.* The Bay of Naples. Thorvaldsen, Thø-ming and other passengers are sitting in the boat in the foreground. 1828.

*

In the show-cases are several personal souvenirs of Thor-valdsen, amongst which are the prize medals won by him at the Danish Academy of Art, his watches and rings, his flute, decorations, the letter conferring upon him the Freedom of the City of Copenhagen (1838), and his small collection of Oriental bronze bowls.

ROOM XXXII

The ceiling decoration is painted by G. C. Hilker; the theme is from Nero's Golden House (formerly called Titus' Baths). It was painted in 1843 and was the first example of this kind of decoration in Thorvaldsen's Museum.

THE LAST, UNFINISHED WORKS OF THORVALDSEN

188 Bust of Martin Luther. Original model. Copenhagen, 1844.
524 Chalk sketch on a slate for the relief, The Genius of Sculpture sitting on the Shoulder of the Statue of Jupiter. Copenhagen, 1844.

OTHER WORKS OF THORVALDSEN

A clockcase, carved in his youth. Presented in 1860 to the Museum by C. A. Ollendorff, Merchant of Holbæk, Zealand.
425 RELIEF. Shepherdess with a Cupid's Nest. Original model. 1831.

598 RELIEF. Christian Charity. Original model. 1810.

630 PORTRAIT MEDALLION. E. H. Løffler, Drawing Master at the Royal Academy of Fine Arts. Copenhagen, 1796. Cast.

634 — Heinrich Reinhold, Painter. Original model.1825. In marble on the memorial to Reinhold, in the Protestant cemetery in Rome.

PAINTINGS

108 *C. G. Carus*. Burial Mound by Moonlight.

112 *F. Catel*. Sunset on a Landscape.

129 *J. A. Koch*. Noah's Sacrifice after the Deluge. 1815.

160A *Louise Seidler*. Fanny Caspers. 1819. Bequeathed by Ministerialrat, Dr. Rudolf von Stankiewicz, Vienna, in 1937.

163 *J. Stieler*. King Ludwig I af Bavaria.

168 *A. Koop*. Copy after *K. Begas'* Portrait of Thorvaldsen (1823). 1828.

188 *J. C. Dahl*. The Shore at Laurvig, Norway. 1840.

189 — From Upper Telemark, Norway. 1840.

191 *Thomas Fearnley*. The Sea at Palermo. 1833.

199A *D. C. Blunck*. Two German Doctors, Fellow Lodgers of Thorvaldsen's during the Cholera Epidemic in Rome 1837.

203 *Heinrich Buntzen*. The Manor of Nysø. 1843.

207 *C. Dahl*. Larsen's Wharf, Copenhagen. 1840.

210 *C. W. Eckersberg*. Harvest Girl in antique Dress. 1813-1816.

211 — Roman Beggar. 1815.

214 — The Piazza of St. Peter's, Rome. 1813-1816.

216 — Frederik VI (1820). A replica, 1839.

217A — The Colosseum, Rome. 1813-1816.

220A *Constantin Hansen.* M. G. Bindesbøll, Architect of the
Museum. 1849. Executed to the order of the Museum Committee.

220C — View of Thorvaldsen's Museum. 1858. Presented
to the Museum in 1938 by C. B. Henriques,
(Danish) King's Counsel.

227 *C. A. Jensen.* The Flower Painter, C. D. Fritzsch.
(C. 1835?).

227A — Baroness Christine Stampe. 1827. Presented by the
Barony of Stampenborg, 1924.

227B — Thorvaldsen. 1839. Presented by Prince and Princess Murat, 1926.

227C — Ludvig Bødtcher, Poet. 1836. Presented by Mrs.
Elisabeth Theodor Jensen, 1942.

245 *A. Küchler.* The Paulsen Family. Thorvaldsen's
Daughter and son-in-law, Colonel Fritz Paulsen.
1838.

258B *Wilh. Marstrand.* Just Mathias Thiele, Thorvaldsen's
biographer. Purchased 1874.

265 *Anton Melbye.* Fishing Vessels in the Channel. 1844.

272 *Ernst Meyer.* Franciscan Friar.

*

The furniture, with canvas-embroidered covers, is from
Thorvaldsen's apartment in Charlottenborg Palace and
was presented to him by a circle of Copenhagen ladies to
commemorate his "Roman" birthday, the 8th March 1840.

ROOM XXXIII

*The ceiling decoration, with a theme from Nero's Golden House
(formerly called Titus' Baths), is executed by G. C. Hilker.*

PLASTER SKETCHES FOR STATUES AND
MONUMENTS

13 A Venus and Cupid. Cast. Loan from the Hirschsprung
Collection, Copenhagen, 1932.

19 A Nemesis. Original model.

49-50   Triumphant Muses. Original models. 1827.

57-58   Sibyls. Original models.

73-81   For the Sermon of John the Baptist. Original
models. (Cf. Nos. 59-70, pp. 28).

84-85   Christ. Original models. Preliminary studies for
the statue in The Church of Our Lady in Copenhagen.

88-109   The Apostles. 88, Matthew. 90, John. 92, James
the Less. 97, Thomas. 100, Bartholomew. 102, Simon
Zelotes. 104, Paul. 106-107, Thaddeus. 109, Andrew.
Original models.

111 and 112 A   The Angel of Baptism. Original models.
(112 A, burnt clay. Bequest from Consul Johan Bravo,
in 1876).

157   The Genii of Life and Death. Original model.

158   The Genii of Life and Death by a Sepulchral Pillar.
Original model.

159   Kneeling Angel. Original model. Nysø 1839.

175   A Hunting Boy. Thorvaldsen's grandson, Albert
Paulsen. Original model. Nysø 1843.

177 A Shepherd Boy. Original model. Bought from the
family Buti, Rome, in 1854.

178 A Dancing Girl. Original model. Purchased 1875.

182   Young Girl Dancing. Original model.

184 Flower Girl. Original model.
185 A Youth with a Dog. Original model.

SKETCHES FOR RELIEFS

118 The Invention of the Printing Press. Original model.
153 Three Genii. Motto of King Christian IV: *Regna firmat pietas*. Like the statue No. 152 (Room XXI) originally intended for the memorial to King Christian IV in Roskilde Cathedral. Original model. Nysø. 1842.
344 Apollo amongst the Shepherds. 1837. Cast.
427 The Ages of Love. 1824. Altered in Copenhagen, 1843. Cast.
546-47 The Genii of the Arts and Handicrafts. Modelled in 1838 from Thorvaldsen's drawings by Pietro Galli for the former Palazzo Torlonia, Rome (later demolished). Casts.
552 Adam and Eve with Cain and Abel. Original model.
554 The Judgment of Solomon. Original model. 1835. A sketch for a projected pediment for the (former) Town Hall-and-Law Courts, Copenhagen.
561 The Resurrection. 1835. A sketch for a projected pediment for Christiansborg Chapel, Copenhagen. Cast.
566 Christ blessing Children. Nysø 1839. Cast.
604 The Abolition of Villeinage in Denmark. Original model. Copenhagen 1842. A sketch for the Frederik VI Monument near Skanderborg, Jutland. (See Nos. 605-610).
605 The Establishment of Provincial Advisory Assemblies in Denmark. Original model. Copenhagen, in the Winter 1842-43. See No. 604.
606 The Administration of Justice. Original model. Copenhagen 1843. See No. 604.

607   The Protection of the Arts and Sciences. Original mo-
      del. Copenhagen, in the Winter 1842-43. See No. 604.
609   Justice and Strength. Original model. Copenhagen
      1843. See No. 604.
617   For the memorial to the Poninski Brother and Sister.
      Original model. 1835.

ROOM XXXIV

*The ceiling is decorated by David Jacobsen and M. M. Goldschmidt
after a theme from Hadrian's Villa.*

649   Marble fireplace with two Caryatids and a Frieze of
      Cupids. Marble (Thorvaldsen).

RELIEF SKETCHES

349-350   The Abduction of Ganymede. Original models.
      1833.
449   Cupid and Psyche. "Farewell to Nysø". Nysø, 24th
      May 1841. Cast.
453   Cupid tying together the Torches of Hymen. Origi-
      nal model. Copenhagen 1840.
550   Denmark praying for her King. Original model. Co-
      penhagen 1839. Sketch for a medal to be made on
      the occasion of Christian VIII's accession to the throne.
574   Christ's Entry into Jerusalem. Original model. 1842.
608   The Abolition of Villeinage in Denmark. For the
      Skanderborg Monument to King Frederik VI. Copen-
      hagen, 1842. Cast. See No. 604 (page 79).
610   Symbols of the Arts and Sciences, wreathed by Genii.
      For the Skanderborg Monument to King Frederik VI.
      Original model. Copenhagen 1843. See No. 607.
648   A Bacchante with a Bird. Original model. 1837.

SKETCHES FOR STATUES AND MONUMENTS

5 A Mercury about to slay Argus. Original model. Purchased 1931.

10 Vulcan. Original model.

15-16 Hercules. Original models.

17-18 Minerva. Original models.

19 Nemesis. Original model.

20-21 Aesculapius. Original models.

15-21 Sketches for the four colossal statues in Prince Jørgen's Courtyard, Christiansborg Palace. Thorvaldsen only lived to complete the Hercules statue (see No. 14, page 53) whilst the others were executed after his death by H. V. Bissen from Thorvaldsen's sketches. Modelled in Copenhagen 1839.

30 The Graces. Original model.

48 Victory. Original model.

113 A Copernicus. Original model. Presented by Marius Nielsen, Esq., in 1922.

117 Gutenberg. Original model. Modelled in Rome, in 1833, by H. V. Bissen under Thorvaldsen's supervision.

120 For a Monument to General Schwarzenberg. Original model. 1821.

133 Lord Byron. Original model.

138 Schiller. 1835. Cast.

139 Goethe. Copenhagen 1840. Cast.

140 Goethe. Original model. Copenhagen 1839.

141 King Frederik VI. Original model. Copenhagen 1840.

148-149 For the Monument to Pope Pius VII in St. Peter's. Original models.

151 Conradin, the last Hohenstaufen Emperor. Original model.

160-61   Luther and Melanchton. Original models. Sketches
         for statues in the Church of Our Lady, Copenhagen.
         Not completed.
163   Thorvaldsen. A sketch for his Self-Portrait (see No.
         162 A, Room XX). Nysø 1839. Cast.
168-169 A Lady, seated. Original models.
170   A Lady, seated, and a Boy. Original model.

ROOM XXXV

*The theme for the ceiling decoration is from Diomedes' Villa in Pompeii
and is executed by J. F. Busch and Magnus Petersen.*

EGYPTIAN ANTIQUES

These objects are tomb finds and for the most part asso-
ciated with burial rites, i.e. intended to serve as a protection and decoration of the mummy whilst in the tomb,
others are funeral accessoires, etc. Some of the objects found
have, however, been in use during the lifetime of the mummy, after which, according to a custom which was general
among the civilizations of Antiquity, they were buried with
the dead so as to be of use to them in the next life. The
large majority of the objects date back to the late Egyptian
period (*c.* 600 B.C. to 300 A.D.), whereas others are from
an earlier period (*c.* 1600 to 1000 B.C.). The earliest period
of Egyptian culture is not represented in the collection.

Cabinet No. 1. In the three upper rows: Deities. The
smallest of them are amulets, the largest served various
religious uses (such as votive offerings, etc.). The fourth
row in cabinet No. 1 and the top row in case No. 2 contain
representations of sacred animals that were the object of
worship and adoration.

Show-cases 2 and 3. Amulets and signets; the latter have

flat reverse sides with sunk signs and figures (plaster casts are on view). The most frequent form is the scarabaeus showing on the upper side the sacred scarab. The material was usually soft stone (steatite) or the so-called Egyptian faience. On the reverse side are carved images of deities, royalties, sacred animals, hieroglyphics representing the names of gods and kings (the great Pharaoh, Thothmes III especially), or various signs for warding off evil and bringing good luck.

Cabinet 4. Jars, drinking cups and vases, mainly of alabaster. Nos. 282-301 were used for ointments and cosmetics. The inscription on No. 301 shows that it was used as a New Year's gift.

Case 5. Finger-rings; those in bronze and silver are provided with signets. Beads, some of which have been threaded in nets, found on mummies, or in neklaces. It is highly probable that some of the beads and the mounted scarabs originate from Italic tomb finds.

Case 6. Nos. 251-252, handles of the metal rattle (called the sistrum) which was used in the worship of Isis. Nos. 253-254, small vessels for ritual purposes. No. 256, a box containing eye black and the stick with which it was applied. No. 257, a bronze mirror.

Cabinet 7 and the two cases beside it contain objects explicitly made for funeral purposes. The tombstones (Nos. 345-349) and the wooden tablet (No. 350) show the dead sacrificing to various deities, or receiving personal homage from their relatives; the hieroglyphic inscriptions contain names and titles as well as religious formulae. Figures 361-381 have been found in large numbers in tombs, enclosed in wooden coffins; they were supposed to do agricultural work for the dead in the next world.

Cases 8-9. Mummy ornaments. Nos. 394-397, breast

ornaments of cloth covered with stucco, painted or gilded. Nos. 398-400, breastplates of faience, painted wood and talc. Nos. 402-411, scarabaei which were placed on the breast of the deceased.

Below: Funeral urns which once contained the separately embalmed intestines of the body; they are to be found, four in number, at the side of the mummy, and usually in a coffin of their own. The lids have the shape of the head of a person, a monkey, a jackal and a falcon, representing the four divine beings which were considered to protect the embalmed body.

Plaster-casts of two Egyptian royal statues (No. 1, Mernephta III. No. 2, King Amenophis III) and of the lid of a mummy sarcophagus (No 3).

Books from Thorvaldsen's library.

ROOM XXXVI

The ceiling is decorated by Heinrich Hansen after a theme from Nero's Golden House (formerly called Titus' Baths). The principal picture is the work of Th. Wegener.

GREEK, ETRUSCAN AND ROMAN ANTIQUES

Cabinet 1. Figures of bronze. Nos. 1-23 and 25-28, *Etruscan.* 2, a goddess. 5, Jupiter, youthful and beardless. 6, Minerva. 8-10, Sileni. 16-19, Palaestrites. 27-28, Lions' Heads, possibly used for tomb decorations. Nos. 24, 29, 32-82, *Greek and Roman.* 32, Athene. 33, Cybele and Atys. 34, Jupiter. 26, Ceres. 38, Apollo. 40, Mars. 41, Venus. 44-46, Mercury. 47, Silenus. 48-49, Priapus. 50, Telesphoros, a Phallic figure, with a cloak covering the upper part of the body. 51-55, Cupid. 61, Atlas. 62-65, the sacrificing Lar (a household god). 69, Hercules. 75, an Actor. The images of deities were either used in the house or were votive offerings to the temples. The other figures served decorative purposes and were placed on vessels or other objects.

Cases 2-3. Figures, heads and masks, etc. of bronze, most of them used to decorate vessels or utensils. No. 29, two lions attacking a hind, Tarento, 4th century B.C.

Cabinet 4. Etruscan bronze mirrors. The fronts were brightly polished. The backs are engraved with various scenes, partly from the life of the gods and Heroes, partly from human life.

Case 5. Finger rings, amulet capsules, buckles, necklaces, bracelets, hairpins, etc. of bronze.

Case 6. Various ornaments, scales and weights, signs, keys, spoons, surgical instruments and forceps, bathscrapers (Nos. 357-358) etc., all of bronze.

Cabinet 7. Ladles, jugs and other household or sacred vessels (Nos. 230-268); lamps (Nos. 304-305G; candelabrum for four candles (No. 306); feet and fittings for different articles of furniture (Nos. 308-328); bells (Nos. 348-350); bath-scrapers (No. 356, 359); various other implements and weapons (Nos. 369-387).

Cabinet 8. Household utensils including sieves (Nos. 259-262); ointment jars (Nos. 269-271); handles of various vessels (Nos. 272-300; No. 283 shows a representation of Scylla of Tarentum, dating from the end of 4th or beginning of 3rd cent. B.C.); feet for vessels (Nos. 301-302); a knife handle in the shape of a table leg (No. 303); arrow-heads (Nos. 378-379); spear and lance heads (Nos. 374-376); ferrule for a lance (No. 377); axes (palstaves) (Nos. 369-379).

Case 9. Objects of ivory and bone. No. 22, game piece. No. 23, a so-called gladiator sign. No. 25, a doll (from the Roman catacombs). Nos. 3-8 and 10 are from Etruscan tombs.

Case 10. II. Jewellery and amulets (Nos. 102-112), fragments of vases (Nos. 117-112) of chalcedony, cornelian, crystal and precious stones. IV. Nos. 3-12, silver amulets and jewellery; No. 4, an arrow-head of flint with silver mounting. VI. Objects of lead. Nos. 20-78 are tokens which were used during the performance of plays, in baths, in the distribution of grain, etc.

Cabinet 11. Nos. 1-68, a bowl, a jug, oil bottles etc. of glass. The multi-coloured objects with molten ornaments show a style originating in Egypt. Nos. 91-94, mosaics of glass. IV. 1. The Roman portrait head of the Emperor Antoninus Pius, is of chased silver. VIII, 1. A Jupiter (Serapis) head of ivory (see the marble statuette No. 2 in Room XXXIX, cabinet No. 1).

Case 12. Glass. Nos. 28-30, fragments of bowls with raised white figures. Nos. 37-42, fragments of handles. Nos. 69-90, fragments of wall and ceiling ornaments. Nos. 95-126, imitations of precious stones (for mounting), beads and links of necklaces.

Case 13. Trinkets of gold, the majority from Etruscan tombs. Nos. 1-16, finger rings; the first three have on the plates, animals of the early Etruscan type. Nos. 17-44, ear-rings. No. 45, a necklace. Nos. 46-54, beads etc. for necklaces or ear-rings. Nos. 55-62, amulet capsules and amulets (No. 61 contains an arrow head of flint, No. 62 a fossil shark's-tooth). No. 64, a bracelet. Nos. 65-75, various trinkets worn on garments (Nos. 66 and 67 have been used for decorating the dead. Nos. 68-74 were probably used as ear-rings).

*

Books from Thorvaldsen's library.

ROOM XXXVII

The Bacchus figure in the ceiling decoration is painted by Th. Wegener.
The remainder is executed by Philip August Fischer after a theme from
Nero's Golden House (formerly called Titus' Baths).

WORKS BY THORVALDSEN

226B BUST. Portrait of a Man. Original model. Purchased
     1898.

240D — Elisa von der Recke, German Poetess. Half-size.
     Original model. C. 1805-06. Purchased 1944.

279A — Rosa Taddei, Italian Improvisatrice. Original
     model. 1826.

280A — J. L. Thrane, Architect. Original model. C. 1805-
     1806.

ANTIQUE GEMS AND PASTES

The show-cases contain cut stones, precious or hard *(gems)*
and glass imitations of such *(pastes)*, all antique.

Those with sunk figures served principally as seals. They
were usually worn on rings; gold rings Nos. 2, 40, 44, 56,
388, 661, and 1053 are antique whilst the remainder are
modern. Nos. 142, 144, 206, 291, 326, 372, 402, 615, 653,
1618 and others have fragments of the antique mountings
in silver, bronze and iron rings. The engraved figures
especially, which are of great variety, must be considered
as seals. The occasional inscriptions are usually the names or
initials of the owner.

1st Class, Nos. 1-59. These are shaped on the reverse side
like a scarab (chafer), a shape adopted from the Egyptians
and especially used in Etruria. Nos. 1-44 are Etruscan, Nos.
53-59 Graeco-Roman.

2nd Class, Nos. 60-81. Engraved in the early (Archaic) style.
3rd Class, Nos. 82-1583. The engravings on these testify

to the fully developed art of the Greeks and Romans. According to the subjects, the gems are arranged in the following groups: the pantheon, the Heroes, historical events, human occupations, animals, and symbolical groupings.

4th Class, Poor or indifferent work, the majority dating from the period when antique art was on the decline. Nos. 1678-1693 belong to the so-called Abraxas Stones, the subjects and inscriptions of which are products of the mysticism and the blending of religions prevailing from the second to the fifth centuries A.D., especially in Syria and Egypt. They were religious symbols and amulets, used by the Gnostics and other sects.

The gems and pastes with figures in relief *(cameos)* were body ornaments (No. 72 is an antique finger ring) and mountings on jewel cases, vases and so forth. Many of them have excellently engraved figures.

*

Casts of antique reliefs are mounted in the walls; on Nos. 275-76 are shown racing-chariots and on the third (No. 278) three civic goddesses.

ROOM XXXVIII

The ceiling is decorated with a theme from Nero's Golden House (formerly called Titus' Baths), executed by Joel Ballin and C. Weber.

ANTIQUE COINS

I. Greek coins. A. Prior to the middle of the 5th century B.C. The coins in this section are all of silver. Gold coins were comperatively rare in this period, and copper (bronze) coins were not yet minted. Some of them, the earliest, are stamped on one side only. The style, as well as the inscriptions, is that peculiar to this period, the so-called Archaic. The greater part are without any inscription or only show the initials of a certain people or city. Of the exhibits the first, which were minted in the Island of Aegina, are among the oldest; they date from the 7th century B.C. *B. From the middle of the 5th century B.C. up to the Roman Empire*. In this period copper coins were im common use, and gold coins were minted more frequently. The coins are more flat and round, and (with few exceptions) stamped on both sides. The stamping shows that Greek style which reached its apex at the beginning of this period. A large number of these coins are characterized by the pure and beautiful artistic style and excellent engravings, such as those from Sicyon, Corinth, Elis, Phocis, Locris, and Macedonia and especially those from Southern Italy and Sicily. The inscriptions are longer and present a variety of subjects; the names of kings and State officials now appear on them. *C. The Roman Empire*. The Greek vassal states and princes rarely minted silver and only occasionally gold. The coins usually bear the head and name of the emperor and his name on one side. Some, especially those stamped after the 2nd century show the decline of art. Like the foregoing, they have Greek inscriptions.

II. Coins of other nations. Of the *Persian* coins, the first four date from the time of the Achaemenides, the kings prior to the conquest of Alexander the Great, the following eight from the time of the Arsacid dynasty, the last two from the Sassanids. The gold and silver coins exhibited *Phoenician* are minted by the Carthagenians after the conquest of Sicily, whose Greek coins they resemble; the admirable execution shows that some of them are the work of Greek engravers, but the inscriptions are Phoenician. The coins minted in Spain by the *Celtiberians* are from the last two centuries B.C. The designs show the influence of Roman minting, but the inscriptions are Celtiberian. The coins of the *Italics* are partly cast, in copper and very heavy, and partly stamped as are the South Italian Greek coins, from which they frequently differ only in that the inscriptions are Etruscan, Umbrian and Oscan. They belong to the era between the 4th and 2nd centuries B.C. The second row contains coins from the barbarian races in Gaul and Pannonia and are mostly imitations of Greek and Roman coins and very crude work.

III. Coins of the Roman Colonies. A. Republican Period. Usually, these have the same stamp as was formerly used in the provinces and cities where they were minted, but the inscriptions are in Latin and the name of Rome or the names and portraits of Roman rulers emphasize the supremacy exerted by Rome. – *B. The Time of the Empire.* These coins also inscribed in Latin, have usually on the obverse the Emperor's or Empress's head and name, and on the reverse the stamp peculiar to the individual countries and cities.

IV. The coins of Rome. A. Republican Period. The earliest coins were of bronze and cast (see the first row), especially the As and its subdivisions which were distinguished from one another by different heads and symbols of divinities; later on they were stamped (see 2nd row). Silver coins, of which the denarius was the most common, were first minted by the Romans, shortly before the first Punic War. These show a wide variety of designs and inscriptions as it was left to the authorities in charge of the minting to choose the designs themselves. – *B. The Time of the Empire.* The obverse usually displays the head of the Emperor or Empress or some other member of the Imperial family, with name and title, whilst the designs on the reverse side vary considerably.

V. Byzantine Coins, minted by the emperors of the Eastern Empire. The earliest coins retain the Roman characteristics, the following show Christian symbols and subjects, and the last have Greek inscriptions.

MORE RECENT MEDALS

The show-case under the window. Medals Nos. 15-25 show reproductions of works by Thorvaldsen. Nos. 26-31 and 131 have been executed by medallists from before Thorvaldsen's time, and Nos. 36-130 and 132-135 by medallists contemporary with Thorvaldsen.

PAINTINGS

1   *Lorenzo Monaco,* Florence, beginning of the 15th century. Mary and Child.

2   *Taddeo di Bartolo,* Siena, *C.* 1400. Predella with scenes from Christ in Gethsemane, the Crucifixion, the Resurrection, Mary Magdalene and St. Catherine.

3   *Italy,* 15th century. Mary and Child.

4   *Fiorenzo di Lorenzo,* Umbria, latter part of 15th century. Two panels from the leaves of a triptych, with pictures of St. Eligius and St. John the Baptist.

5   *School of Pinturicchio,* Umbria, 15th century. Mary and Child.

10   Attributed to *Francesco Bassano the Younger,* Venice, latter part of 16th century. Evening Domestic Tasks.

16   *Giovanni Battista Salvi,* called *Sassoferrato,* Rome, 17th century. Mary, praying.

20   *Giovanni Francesco Barbieri,* called *Guercino,* Bologna, 17th century. A Young Girl, reading.

44   Attributed to *Pieter Breughel the Younger,* called Hell Breughel. Netherlands, 16-17th centuries. Hell.

50 *Dutch,* 17-18th centuries. Landscape in the style of
G. Dughet. Probably by *J. F. van Bloemen.*

*

On the cabinet in the background containing the rest of the
collection of antique coins, is a bust of Thorvaldsen in
marble executed by an unidentified artist.

ROOM XXXIX

In the ceiling decoration the centre picture, Psyche pleading with Venus, is
executed by Th. Wegener. The rest, a theme from Nero's Golden House
(formerly called Titus' Baths), is the work of C. F. Sørensen.

ANTIQUE SCULPTURES OF MARBLE, TERRA-COTTA

Left side wall. Chiefly Roman marble sculpture. *On the*
brackets: No. 7, Mercury, head, Roman copy after a Greek
original from the 4th century B.C.–Nos. 13-14, Heads of
Satyrs. – No. 24, Head of a Pudicitia Statue (limestone).–
No. 29, Trunk of a Young Man. No. 37, Apotheosis of the
Emperor Hadrian (marble work from the 18th century).–
No. 39, Portrait of the Emperor Septimius Severus, 2-3rd
centuries A.D.–No. 40, Portrait, and of 1st century A.D.–
No. 47, Idealized Portrait of a Woman. – No. 82, Fragment
of the support of a marble table from the middle of the 2nd
century B.C.–Nos. 83-84, architectural fragments with sculpture on both sides, on No. 83 a Cyclops head. *Sunk into the*
wall: No. 76, fragment of a Greek votive relief for Asklepios
(Aesculapius), 4th century B.C.–No. 77, Monkey eating a
Turnip, fragment of an architectural relief slab.–No. 90,
fragment of a Greek sepulchral relief showing a farewell
scene, 4th century B.C. *At the bottom:* No. 5, the right leg
of an Apollo statue with a Griffin at the side, with traces
of red colour. No. 18, Head of Pan.–No. 92, mortuary urn.

Cabinet 1. Chiefly Roman marble sculpture. No. 1, Cybele.–No. 4, Minerva, a representation inspired by Greek works from *c.* 450 B.C.–No. 6, the Ephesian Artemis (Diana).–No. 11, Bacchus, a representation inspired by Greek works from *c.* 500 B.C.–No. 12, Mercury, Roman work in the early Greek style. Nos. 20-22, Aesculapius.–No. 25, Woman's Head of basalt, 5th century A.D.–No. 28, Trunk of Statuette, the guardian deity of Antiochia, Roman repetition of *Eutychides'* original statue (3rd century B.C.).–No. 32, Trunk of a Jupiter Serapis statuette, a representation inspired by *Bryaxis'* colossal statue in Alexandria (4th century B.C.).–No. 34, Head of a Youth, Roman work in the style of *Polyclitus.*–No. 45, Head of a Roman Lady (polished quart).–No. 50, fragment of the statue of an athlete, so-called Diadumenos, Roman copy of an original by *Polyclitus* (5th century B.C.).–No. 67, Greek sculpture showing Cybele in a Temple.–No. 74, A Diana relief. *On top of the cabinet:* No. 35, Head of a Youth, Roman copy of an original in the style of *Polyclitus.*–No. 36, Head of a Demosthenes statue, Roman copy of an original by *Polyeuctus* (3rd century B.C.).–No. 48, late Roman portrait of a Boy, 2-3rd centuries A.D.

Cabinet 2. Terra-cotta. Figures and heads like Nos. 1-13 and Nos. 26-34 were mainly used as votive offerings and sacrificial gifts. The latter were buried with the dead, the votive offerings were kept in the temples. Some of them represent goddesses whereas others, ilke the Italic heads (Nos. 6-10) show mortals being placed under the protection of a deity. The enthroned goddesses, Nos. 1-3 are in the Greek Archaic style. The draped female figures, Nos. 18-24 belong to the group set up in the house for decorative purposes and afterwards buried with the dead. Nos. 6-13 and 44 are Etruscan-Italic. All the other figures are Greek. No.

263 is a small Etruscan-Italic altar, and Nos. 264-66 are Roman lamp stands.

Right side wall. Terra-cotta. *On the bracket:* facing tiles and waterspouts, three of which in the shape of theatrical masks (Nos. 53-55). *Sunk into the wall:* Fragments of friezes which were placed on the walls of temples, houses and tombs; the majority have been found in the environs of Rome. Most of them are Roman work executed from Greek models; some imitate the early Greek style, viz. those of the female temple servants (Nos. 65-66) and the Gorgon faces (Nos. 120-123). *Under the case:* three large frieze slabs with scenes from the Exploits of Hercules (Nos. 96-98).

Cases 3-4. Roman clay lamps of the Empire period. Nos. 249 and 250 belong to the Christian period. Nos. 256-262 are imitations, intended for funeral purposes.

Case 5. Figures and heads, some of which belonged to larger objects, whilst others were toys (Nos. 47-50 are perhaps Greek), masks which were placed on coffins (Nos. 270-71 are Etruscan, from Campania), vessels, and lamps. Fragments of red Aretine pottery, etc.

On the window wall a relief figure of marble (Apollo?) and a Roman mosaic.

ROOM XL

The ceiling decoration is executed by C. F. Sørensen after a theme from Nero's Golden House (formerly called Titus' Baths).

GREEK, ITALIC AND ETRUSCAN POTTERY

Although relatively comprehensive, this collection of vessels with painted figures and ornaments – usually described as vases – does not give even an approximate idea of the development of Greek pottery and its variety of styles. It was collected in Rome and contains, therefore, only those groups of Greek vases which, regularly and in quantity, were imported into Central Italy at a time when Greek art and applied art were at their highest, in the 6th and 5th centuries B.C., and the market in Italy was completely dominated by the Greek ceramic art. The pottery made by the various Italian peoples at that time, and especially by the most prominent of them, the Etruscans, was much cruder and simpler than the exquisite Greek vases. The attempts occasionally made by the Etruscans to imitate these show more than anything else how very far behind the Greeks they actually were, both technically and artistically; samples of such imitations are to be found under No. 47 in cabinet *No. 1* and No. 151 on top of cabinet *No. 2*. These Greek imports only dropped off from *c.* 400 B.C., as a consequence of the political crisis in Greece and the ensuing unmistakable decline in trade and industry. For yet another hundred years, painted vases continued to be used in Italy but they were now made in the country itself, in Etruria, Campania and the large Greek colonies in Southern Italy.

The vases exhibited have all, or nearly all, been found in tombs in Etruria or neighbouring districts, where the ancient custom was to bury them with the dead to be used by them in the next world. They were not specifically made for burial purposes as may be seen from the fact that the very same vessels and others of the same kind were commonly used in everyday life. Although found and used in Etruria, they are purely Greek in nature and style. The various forms (drinking bowls, jugs, wine jars, ointments jars, etc.) reflect the domestic habits of the Greeks. The technique and decoration testify to the high standard of Greek craftsmanship–and regardless of all attempts the deep black lustre possessed by Greek pottery has only

7

been imitated in quite recent times; the subjects of the pictures are Greek legends and scenes from Greek everyday life.

In the 6th and 5th centuries B.C. Athens was the largest exporter to Etruria and as a natural result Attic vases form the greater part of the Greek vases in the collection. Corinth (Nos. 1-8, 160-161) and Chalcis (Nos. 70 and 80) are not so well represented.

Cabinet 1, to the left.

At the top: Corinthian vases and Italic imitations from the 7th and 6th centuries B.C., the earliest of the groups of vases on exhibit, characterized by the light yellowy clay and the brownish-black varnish. The chief subjects in the decoration are real or fabulous animals (No. 7, ointment jar with a picture of a Siren, i.e. a bird with a human head), on the larger vessels often placed together in friezes (No. 1, deep drinking bowl: animal frieze with panthers, sphinxes and griffins). – *Below* are two rows of Attic vases from the 6th century B.C., with black figures on a yellowish-red ground. The women's flesh is usually painted white. The following pictures may be mentioned. No. 27, Silenus, with a Drinking Horn, bending under the weight of a large wine basin which he is carrying on his back. – No. 10, Dionysus, ivy-crowned and with a large wine beaker and vines in his hands. A series of the great Labours of Hercules: No. 44, The Struggle with Apollo for the Delphian tripod. – No. 41, The fight with Triton. – No. 40, His fight with the Nemean lion. – No. 38 (by the "Antimenes Painter"), Hercules bringing the Erymanthian boar to Eurystheus. – No. 42, The fight with the Amazons: – No. 39, Hercules taming the Cretan bull. – *Below:* Two rows of dark clay vessels with faintly shining black surfaces ("Bucchero"), a

remarkable ceramic that reached a specially high degree
of perfection in Etruria in the 7th and 6th centuries B.C.

Cabinet 1, to the right.
Above and in the middle: Chiefly Attic vases (No. 47, Etruscan imitation) from the 6th century B.C., with black
figures on a yellowish-red ground. In most cases the pictures
are roughly executed. Many of them portray Bacchic scenes, viz. Nos. 16, 26, 29, 31, and 34. Theseus' fight with the
monster Minotaurus is to be seen on the amphora No. 47
and the drinking bowl No. 48. – *Below:* Pottery of various
periods, principally Italian work. Two of them (Nos. 281
and 282) date back to 7-6th centuries B.C.

Cabinet 2.
Above and in the middle: Attic vases from the 6th century
B.C., with figures on a yellowish-red ground. Among the
most important are three water jars (hydriae) decorated
with pictures of a mythical (i.e. not real) wedding procession (No. 74), a four-in-hand, seen from the front (No. 54,
by the "Antimenes Painter") and a war chariot in battle
(no. 56, ascribed to the so-called "Leagros Group"); the
driver is distinguishable by his long white garb. No. 52, a
well-preserved amphora with a frequently occurring, some-
what schematically executed picture: two Heroes in battle,
at the right and left a woman onlooker. – *Below:* Pottery,
varnished all black, from 4th-2nd centuries B.C., made in
different Italic workshops, especially in Etruria and Campania. The shapes mostly imitate those of metal vessels.

Cabinets 3-4.
Above and in the middle: Vases from the heyday of Attic
ceramic art, *c.* 530-400 B.C., with light-coloured figures
7*

reserved in the colour of the clay against a dark background. The most important steps in the stylistic development are represented, from the strictly Archaic art with its conventional representation of the human body to the free delvelopment of art about and after the middle of the 5th century B.C. At this time the favourite subjects for vase painting were scenes from everyday life such as the athletic exercises of young Greeks (see the drinking bowls Nos. 107 and 111 which are executed by the "Foundry Painter", and 112 which is the work of the »Brygos Painter"), their intercourse with young women (the bowl No. 114, which is attributed to the "Penthesilea Painter", the amphora No. 117) and scenes from their drinking bouts (the bowl No. 115 after which a series of vases is named "The Thorvaldsen Group"). However, there are also mythical and heroic pictures: Ajax and Achilles playing a table game (the drinking bowl No. 100, which is executed by the vase painter *Oltos)*; the Punishment of Actaeon (amphora No. 99, by the "Geras Painter"). From an artistic point of view the best, apart from Nos. 100, 111-12 and 114, are two fragments of large mixing bowls (craters), No. 96 by the "Altamura Painter" picturing Poseidon and a goddess, and No. 97 (which, like No. 101 originated from the circle of the vase painter, *Polygnotos),* with Dionysus and Dithyrambos. – *Below:* Vases from the 4th and 3rd centuries B.C. with light-coloured figures reserved in the colour of the clay against a background of dark glaze, the majority Italic work from workshops in Etruria, Campania, Apulia and Lucania. The dull, carelessly drawn decoration, the uninteresting, often trivial pictures and the poor technique show that the vessels are products of an art on the decline.

*   *   *

BASEMENT

THE EARLY WORKS OF THORVALDSEN AND HIS COLLECTIONS OF CASTS, PAINTINGS AND WATER-COLOURS, ETC.

THORVALDSEN'S EARLY WORKS

ROOM XLIII

At the bottom of the staircase.

654 STATUETTE. Bacchus and Ariadne. Original model. Rome 1798.

657 — Achilles and Penthesilea. Original model. Rome 1801. Bequest from J. M. Thiele, 1875.

661 BUST. Count A. P. Bernstorff. Danish Prime Minister. Presumably an original model. Copenhagen 1795. Presented by the Ministry of the Interior, 1922.

662 — Count A. P. Bernstorff. Original model. Remodelled in Rome 1797, from No. 661.

673 RELIEF. A gateway decoration. Carved in wood by Thorvaldsen in Copenhagen 1792, from a design by the maritime sculptor, F. C. Willerup, for 17 Ny Vestergade, Copenhagen. Presented by the Zealand Farmers Savings Bank, 1936.

674 — The Royal Arms, from the Court Chemists, 25 Store Kongensgade, Copenhagen. Painted sandstone. Copenhagen 1789. Presented by Mr. Ibsen, Court Chemist, in 1882.

689 PORTRAIT-MEDALLION. E. H. Løffler, Drawing Master at the Royal Academy of Fine Arts. Original

model. Copenhagen 1796. Presented by the sculptor, Professor E. Utzon-Frank, in 1926.

ROOM XLIV

672 RELIEF. Cupid, resting. Original model. Copenhagen 1789. Awarded the Art Academy's large silver medal. Presented by the Royal Academy of Fine Arts, in 1855.

675 — Heliodor being driven from the Temple. Original model. Copenhagen. 1791. Awarded the Art Academy's small gold medal. Presented by the Royal Academy of Fine Arts, in 1918.

676 — Achilles an Priam. Original model. Copenhagen 1791. Presented by the Royal Academy of Fine Arts, in 1887.

683 — The Seasons of the Year. Original model. Copenhagen 1794. Executed for Prince Frederik's, later King Christian X's, Palace at Amalienborg from a composition by N. Abildgaard. Loan from the Royal Gallery of Fine Arts, in 1925.

684 — The Parts of the Day. Original model. Copenhagen 1794. Executed for Prince Frederik's, later King Christian X's, Palace at Amalienborg from a composition by N. Abildgaard. Loan from the Royal Gallery of Fine Arts, in 1925.

ROOM XLV

651 STATUETTE. Mother with two Children. Original model. Copenhagen c. 1793. Bought at the auction over the effects of the painter N. Abildgaard, in 1850.

652 STATUETTE. Euterpe, the Muse. Original model, painted plaster. Copenhagen 1794. Preliminary work for the statue in Prince Frederik's, later King Christian X's, Palace at Amalienborg, from a composition by the Royal Academy of Fine Arts, 1855.

653 — Terpsichore, the Muse. Original model, painted plaster. Copenhagen 1794. Preliminary work for the statue in Prince Frederik's, later King Christian X's, Palace at Amalienborg, from a composition by N. Abildgaard. Presented by the Royal Academy of Fine Arts, 1855.

656 — Venus and Cupid. Original model. C. 1800.

677 RELIEF. Hercules and Omphale. Copenhagen 1792. Cast.

678 — The Apostles Peter and John healing the lame Beggar outside the Temple Gate. Original model. Copenhagen 1793. Awarded the Art Academy's large gold medal. Presented by the Royal Academy of Fine Arts, 1918.

682 — King Numa Pompilius in conversation with Egeria, the water nymph, in her Grotto. Copenhagen 1794. Cast.

679 PORTRAIT MEDALLION. Louisa Augusta, Duchess of Augustenburg. Original model, painted and gilded plaster. Copenhagen 1793. Purchased 1911.

680 — Michael Rosing, Danish Actor. Copenhagen 1793. Painted plaster. Purchased 1910.

681 — Johanne Catherine Rosing, née, Olsen, Actress, wife of the above. Copenhagen 1793. Painted plaster. Purchased 1910.

685 — Simon Jensen, Book-keeper and Administrator in the Danish West Indian Trading Company. Original model. Copenhagen 1793.

686 PORTRAIT MEDALLION. Eleonora Maria Jensen, née
     Weygaard, wife of the above. Original model.
     Copenhagen 1793.

687 — The Children of the above; to the left, Anna Bir-
     gitte Margrethe (married name: Glahn). Original
     model. Copenhagen 1793.

685-87 were presented to the Museum by C. J. Glahn,
     manufacturer, assessor pharmaciae, in 1856.

688 PORTRAIT MEDALLION. Count A. P. Bernstorff.
     Original model, painted and gilded plaster. Co
     penhagen 1796. Purchased 1911.

690 — P. J. Monrad, Deputy of the Chancellery, later
     (Danish) Privy Councillor. Painted plaster. Copen-
     hagen. Probably a cast.

691 — Cecilia Kirstine Monrad, née Martin, wife of the
     above. Painted plaster. Copenhagen. Probably a cast.

692 — Probably Bernt Anker, (Danish) Privy Councillor.
     Burnt clay. Original model. Copenhagen. Bought
     1879 from the estate of C. F. Wilckens, the first
     attendant at the Museum.

A 896 — Holger Christian Reiersen, (Danish) Privy Coun-
     cillor. Original model (?). Painted plaster. Copen-
     hagen, 1793. Purchased 1953.

A 897 — Charlotte Kirstine Reiersen, née Studsgaard; wife
     of the above. Original model (?). Painted plaster.
     Copenhagen, 1793. Purchased 1953.

ROOM XLVI

655 STATUE. Pollux. Copy, approximately one third the
     size, of one of the antique horse tamers. Monte
     Cavallo, Rome. Original model. 1799.

663 BUST. Tyge Rothe, Philosopher. Copenhagen 1796. Marble (Thorvaldsen, Rome 1797). Presumably Thorvaldsen's first work in marble.

664 — Mrs. Høyer, the mother of C. F. Høyer, the painter, 1809. Marble (Thorvaldsen). Bequest from the painter C. F. Høyer, 1855.

665 — Raphael. Marble (Thorvaldsen, 1800). Copy of the bust in the Pantheon, Rome.

666 — Agrippa. Marble (Thorvaldsen, 1799-1800). Copy of an antique bust.

667 — Cicero. Marble (Thorvaldsen, 1799-1800). Copy of an antique bust.

668 — Cicero. Marble (Thorvaldsen, 1799-1800). Copy of an antique bust.

669 — Homer. Marble (Thorvaldsen, 1799). Copy of an antique bust.

Nos. 665 and 669 were bought at the auction over the effects of the widow of the painter, N. Abildgaard in 1850 and Nos. 666-68 were presented to the Museum by the Royal Academy of Fine Arts in 1855.

* * *

ROOMS XLVII-XLVIII

An exhibition of plaster casts of Thorvaldsen's works made in the plaster workshop of the Museum. See the separate sales catalogue.

* * *

THORVALDSEN'S COLLECTION OF CASTS

*In corridors A and B, Rooms XLIX, LX, and LXI and part of the storage
gallery is Thorvaldsen's collection of casts of the works of other artists,
mainly antique sculpture but a few from modern times. The collection
gives an interesting picture of the works of art upon which Thorvaldsen
and his contemporaries based their conception of art.*

CORRIDOR A

I. ANTIQUE STATUES AND STATUETTES

Nos. 6 and 7 are two female statues from the Aphaia Temple,
Aegina. The two figures, which originally flanked the
great palmetto acroterium on the western gable of the
Temple, were excavated in 1811, together with many
other fragments of sculpture. The whole of this find was
acquired by King Ludwig of Bavaria (then Crown Prince),
who commissioned Thorvaldsen to restore the pediment
groups (1816-17). The "Archaic" pose and treatment of the
draping of these statuettes possibly influenced Thorvaldsen's
own statue of "Hope" (Room VIII). The sculptures of the
Aphaia Temple were executed about 490-80 B.C. and is
now in the Glyptotheca Gallery, Munich. – No. 8, the hel-
meted Head of a warrior from the east gable of the same
temple, which also contained scenes from the War of the
Aeginettes with Troy.

Nos. 26, 27 and 28 are fragments from the Parthenon
Temple on the Acropolis, Athens. The horse's head and
the upper part of the group with the three seated women
are from the east pediment of the temple, which contained
representations of the birth of Athene. From the west pediment which depicted Athene's dispute with Poseidon over
the Attic country, is the trunk of a reclining man (No. 28),
usually called Ilissos. The Parthenon gables were completed
about 432 B.C. The originals were acquired, in 1801-03,

by Lord Elgin and were included in the British Museum, London, in 1816.

No. 29, the so-called Weber-Laborde head is assumed to originate from the east pediment of the Parthenon. In the time of Thorvaldsen it was in Venice, now it is in Paris.

No. 31, statue of the resting Apollo, the so-called Apollino in Florence. – No. 32, Venus Medici in Florence, and No. 33, the Capitolian Venus belong to works from the last decades of the 4th century; both show the Goddess of Love rising from the sea or the bath. – No. 34, a little kneeling Aphrodite in the bath, is the work of the Hellenistic sculptor *Doidalsas*. In the Vatican. – No. 35, Cupid drawing his Bow, has been attributed to *Lysippus,* the last important sculptor at the 4th century. – No. 36, Two Children kissing one another (Cupid and Psyche). A group from the Hellenistic period. In the Museo Capitolino, Rome. – No. 37, the so-called Psyche from Capua, perhaps the remainder of an Aphrodite statue. The original is in Naples. – No. 39 is a pasticcio (which denotes a statue which a modern restorer has haphazardly put together from separate fragments. Such pasticci were oftentimes made in the workshops of Italian sculptors at the time of the Baroque, and later). The head is a repetition of the Hermes Belvedere (No. 38 in Corridor B.). The trunk, however, belongs to a statue from the 5th century B.C., *Polyclitus'* so-called Diadumenos, showing a Greek athlete binding the Band of Victory round his head. This pasticcio is now in Munich. – Nos. 41 and 42, two statues of Muses, both from the Hellenistic period; in the Glyptotheca of Munich and in the Vatican respectively. – No. 43, upper part of a female figure with a wreath of flowers in her hair. Found in Hadrian's Villa, now in the Capitoline Museum, Rome. – No. 46, head and breast of the so-called Westmacott Ephebe: in the British Museum,

London. Roman copy after *Polyclitus.*–No. 48, Discus Thrower, attributed to the sculptor *Naucydes,* who worked in the first part of the 4th century. This excellent statue, which was found in 1792 near the Via Appia in Rome, is now in the Vatican. The head is antique but belongs to another work.–No. 49. The Thorn Extractor, bronze statue in Palazzo dei Conservatori, Rome, shows a peculiar mingling of Archaic characteristics and a later, more highly developed sense of composition.–No. 50, a little Girl playing *astragalos* (Dice); Hellenistic figure, now in Berlin.–No. 52, a Boy with a Bunch of Grapes in his arms. The original was formerly in the possession of Capece Latro, Archbishop of Tarento, and King Christian VIII of Denmark, and is now in the National Museum, Copenhagen.–No. 53, a Boy eating Grapes.–No. 56, Trunk of a Boy, possibly Ganymede; 4th century, now in Berlin.–No. 57, Roman copy after a Trunk from the first half of the 5th century B.C.; the long curls on the shoulder seem to indicate that this is an Apollo statue. The original is at the Villa Albani, Rome.–No. 58, Trunk of a Youth, now in Berlin. –No. 59, Trunk of a Boy, running.–No. 60, Trunk of a female figure in the *style of Praxiteles,* in Munich.–No. 61, small Trunk of a female figure found by the Danish archaeologist P. O. Brøndsted in the island of Keos, in the Karthaian ruins.–No. 62, Trunk of a female figure, now in the Tegel Palace near Berlin.–Nos. 93 and 94, two Horses' Heads, the first in Florence, the second from the Younger Balbus' equestrian statue, now in Naples.–No. 95, an Eagle with outspread Wings.

No. 266, fragment of a relief with a Horseman. Boeotian sepulchral monument from the time of the Parthenon sculptures and influenced by them. The original, which once belonged to the painter Camuccini, is now in the Vatican.

2. ANTIQUE BUSTS AND HEADS

No. 99, Jupiter from Otricoli; in the Vatican.–No. 100, Poseidon Head in the Vatican; Hellenistic.–No. 112, Head of the so-called Pallas Athene from Velletri; now in the Louvre, Paris.–No. 104, Head of the Apollo Belvedere (see No. 30, Room XLIX).–No. 105, Apollo; in the British Museum, London.–No. 106, Venus.–No. 107, Venus, found in Diocletian thermae in 1805; now in the Vatican.–No. 109, Apollo, the original is in the Capitoline Museum, Rome.–Nos. 110 and 112, two herms of Zeus Ammon (in the Vatican) and the bearded Dionysus respectively.– No. 113, Dionysus Head from the 4th century B.C., in the Capitoline Museum.–Nos. 114-16, Satyrs (114 and 115 now in Munich). –No. 117, Head of a Pan statue, in the British Museum, London.–No. 118, Bacchante.–No. 119, a bearded River God or Rural God. Mask.–No. 120, Mask of a head at the Villa Albani, entitled Zeus and rather questionably attributed to *Phidias*.–No. 121, Roma; characterized by reliefs of she-wolves on both sides of the Helmet.–Nos. 123-24, two colossal Heads of the so-called Horse-tamers, now erected on Monte Cavallo, Rome; Hadrian's time.– No. 127, Paris with the Phrygian Cap.–Nos. 128-29, Heads from the famous Laocoon Group in the Vatican; 128, Laocoon himself; 129, the left of the Sons, looking at his Father with a terrified expression. – Nos. 130-133, four Heads from the great Niobide group in Florence. No. 130, Niobe herself; 131, one of her daughters; 132-33, two of her sons. The group is probably the work of *Scopas,* from the middle of the 4th century.–No. 134, a Hero.–No. 135 was formerly called Alexander, but is more likely a dying Hero, in the grandiose pergamum style–No. 136, Mask of the head of an Amazon, perhaps from "Amazone Mattei" in the Vatican.–No. 199, ideal female Head.

Greek Portraits: Nos. 137-38, two ideal Heads of the blind Homer; both after a bust in Naples, 137, however, has been changed a great deal in details.–No. 142, The Cynic, Antisthenes; possibly cast from an example in Naples.–No. 143, Theophrastus, the philosopher; mask of a herm at the Villa Albani, Rome.–No. 144, Posidonius, the Stoic and naturalist; in Naples.–No. 146, Demosthenes. the Orator.–No. 147, Mask at the Villa Albani; formerly called Hannibal.–No. 149, Mask with an Attic helmet, now in the Louvre, Paris; formerly called Miltiades.–No. 150, Head of Alexander the Great from the so-called Alexander Rondanini statue in Munich, restored by Thorvaldsen.–No. 154, Hellenistic Prince (Antiochus III of Syria?); in the Louvre, Paris.–No. 175, Crysippus, the Stoic; in the Capitoline Museum, Rome.–No. 176, Elderly Man, so-called portrait of Seneca.–No. 180, Hellenistic(?) warrior; in Naples.–No. 182, Head of the Diomedes statue at the Glyptotheca, Munich; probably originates from an original by *Cresilas.*–No. 185, Menander, the playwright.–No. 195, Unknown man with Helmet; at the Villa Albani, Rome.– No. 200, female portrait Herm; at the Galleria geografica in the Vatican.

Roman Portraits: No. 157, Head of a Priest; in the Vatican. –Nos. 177, 178 and 179 are unidentified portraits of men: 178 is at the Villa Albani, Rome.–No. 203, an African athlete, head of a statue of black marble in Vienna.

3. ANTIQUE RELIEFS

No. 267, Fragment. Gaea entrusting the small Erichtonios to Athene. At the side, a foot of Hephaestus. The original is in the Vatican.–No. 268, Greek sepulchral monument (stele) for a young man who is shown reading a roll; beginning of 4th century B.C. In the Grotta Ferrata near Rome.

–Nos. 270-71, Dancing Girls, in the Neo-Attic style; now in the Palazzo degli Uffizi, Florence.–No. 274, Neo-Attic relief with a theme from the balustrade of the Nike Temple in Athens; the Uffizi in Florence.–No. 277, two veiled Women, one sitting on a rock, the other standing. In the Vatican.–No. 279, Farewell scene from a tomb relief. A Youth and a sorrowing Woman. In the Vatican.–No. 280, Greek votive relief from the end of the 5th or the beginning of the 4th centuries B.C. In the Vatican. The relief is dedicated (by the little man on the left) to two divinities, a man, seated, who has presumably held a sceptre and a woman, standing, whose figure may have been in Thorvaldsen's mind when he executed his statue of "Hebe" (Room VI, No. 38).–No. 281, a Youth between two Hetaerae, Roman copy after a Hellenistic original. In Naples.–No. 304, Rural idyll. Relief from 1st century A.D. In the Vatican.–No. 306, Cupid driving two wild Boars; at the side, an altar. In the Vatican. Nos. 341-42, Wedding scene. Casts of Roman terracotta (so-called Campana) reliefs.–No. 345, Satyr and Menad. Campana relief in the Villa Albani, Rome.

4. WORKS OF ART FROM MODERN TIMES

No. 3, *Andrea del Verrochio's* half-length portrait of Cosimo de Medici. Alto-relievo. The original in marble in Berlin. –No. 6, Christ on his way to Calvary, relief by *Giovanni da Bologna*. The original in bronze in the Church of SS. Annunziata, Florence.–No. 7, A pan decorated with an outer circle of Tritons, Nereids and Sea Monsters, an inner circle of four River Gods, and in the middle a medal with the portrait of Charles I, Duke of Mantua. Italy, 17th century. –No. 10, *François Duquesnoy* (?), A Figure of a floating Child.–No. 11, A Figure of a floating Child. 17th century.

CORRIDOR B

1. ANTIQUE STATUES

No. 5, She-Wolf, the symbol of Rome. Bronze statue in the Capitoline Museum. Here, without the original's suckling twins, which have no antique authenticity, but are a Renaissance restoration.–No. 38, the Hermes Belvedere, in the Vatican. This famous figure can be traced back to *Praxiteles.*–No. 40, Silenus, holding the little Bacchus on his Arm. The original is probably from the School of *Lysippus.* Louvre, Paris.–No. 45, Ganymede as a Child, having been caught by the Eagle. In the Vatican.–No. 47, the so-called Borghese Fencer, a Hellenistic work now in the Louvre, Paris.–No. 51, A Boy, seated, with a Duck. –No. 55, The Belvedere Trunk, probably representing a Silenus, sitting. Hellenistic. The original in the Vatican.

2. ANTIQUE BUSTS AND HEADS

Roman Portraits. No. 152, the so-called L. Junius Brutus, the first Consul of Rome; bronce bust in the Palazzo dei Conservatori, Rome.–No. 153, the so-called Brutus minor, Cæsar's Murderer. Bust in the Capitoline Museum, Rome. –No. 154, Augustus, the Emperor, as a young Man; originates from Velletri, now on a Toga statue in the Louvre, Paris.–No. 156, Augustus, the Emperor; bronze head in the Vatican library in Rome.–No. 159, A Roman (previously called Galba); mask, in the Louvre, Paris.–No. 160-161, Trojan, the Emperor; No. 160, in the Louvre, Paris; 161 is from a lost original.–No. 162, Aelius Verus; in the Louvre, Paris.–No. 167, Antoninus Pius, the Emperor. The back of the head is missing. From a replica of the head in Sala a Croce Greca in the Vatican.–No. 168, Marcus Aurelius as a Young Man; in the Museo Capitolino, Rome.–No.

169, the above, at a later age.–No. 171, the above, in colossal size. The head of the equestrian statue in the Capitoline Museum, Rome.–No. 172, Lucius Verus, the Emperor; mask.–No. 174, Caracalla, the Emperor; Naples–No. 181, Young man with curly locks and whiskers.–Nos. 183, 184, 188, 189 (in Florence), and 192, Elderly, clean-shaved men. –No. 196, An unidentified Woman, portrayed in a statue of the so-called Pudicitia type.–No. 197, A small female bust from the Claudian period.–No. 198, the Empress Sabina, Hadrian's Consort. In the Museo Capitolino, Rome.

3. ANTIQUE RELIEFS

No. 294, Vase with dancing Menads. At the Villa Albani, Rome.–No. 295, Vase with dancing Satyrs and Corybantes; in the Vatican.–No. 297, Jupiter, Minerva and Apollo. Roman work of art.–No. 298, A puteal (i.e. parapet round a well) with subjects from the Hylas and Narcissus legends. As regards the Hylas legends, see Thorvaldsen's relief with the same theme, No. 484 in Room XIV.

ROOM XLIX

Antique Statue. No. 30, the Apollo Belvedere, famous since the days of the Renaissance, is considered to be the work of *Leochares* from the last half of the 4th century B.C. The god, Apollo–the averter of evil–strides quickly forward and must be imagined holding a bow and arrow in his left hand and the sacred laurel bough in his right hand. In the Vatican, Rome. It is well known to what extent Thorvaldsen was influenced by this statue when executing his statue of "Jason".

Antique Busts. No. 165, Antinous, Hadrian's favourite,

as Bacchus. In the Vatican, Rome.–No. 170, Marcus Aurelius, the Emperor; colossal size, appears to go back to the
equestrian statue in the Capitol, Rome.

ROOM L

180 STATUE. *Thorvaldsen:* Young Girl dancing. 1837.
     Marble.

PAINTINGS

103 *Abraham Teerlink.* Italian Landscape.

221 *H. Harder.* Landscape near Sorø, Zealand.

222 *Julius Hellesen.* Danish Landscape. 1843.

229 *Johs. Jensen.* Old Sailor. 1843.

240 *F. C. Kiærskou.* Scene from the Bavarian Tyrol. 1846.

250 *G. E. Libert.* Heath Landscape near Aalborg, Jutland.
     1839.

257 *Th. Læssøe.* Valløby Church, Zealand. 1839.

260 *H. D. C. Martens.* View of St. Peter's from Via sacra,
     North of Rome.

261 — View of the Capitol from the colonnade in the
     Palazzo dei Conservatori, Rome.

264 *Anton Melbye.* A Dutch Koff and Line-of-Battle Ship
     in a Top-Sail Breeze.

289 *G. Schleisner.* Genre Picture. 1838.

294 *F. Thöming.* An American Brig anchored in the
     Bay of Naples. 1827.

PAINTINGS ROOM LI

70 *F. Diofebi*. The Side Entrance to the Church of Sta.
    Maria in Aracoeli, from the Capitol, Rome. 1825.
71 — The Ruins of the Mars Ultor Temple, Rome. 1826.
81 *Beniamino de Francesco*. Italian Landscape with mytho-
    logical figures, the Sibyl and Aeneas. 1838.
83 *E. Landesio*. Italian Landscape. 1838.
99 *James Severn*. Italian Woman with her Daughter. 1831.
124 *Leo von Klenze*. The Harbour of Pirano, Istria.
133 A *Fr. Nerly*. Italian Landscape.
174 *J. N. Glowački*. Landscape from Tyrol. 1835.
175 *Orest Kiprenskij*. Armenian Priest.
275 *J. Mohr*. Landscape from Bavaria. 1840.

ROOM LII

RELIEF. Below the window. *H. E. Freund:* Selene, the
Goddess of the Moon. Model (plaster) for the capital of the
pilaster on the main front of the Museum, executed in
sandstone by *Johann Scholl* in 1843.

PAINTINGS

86 A *M. Pacetti*. Scene from the River Tiber with the Castle
    of S. Anglo and St. Peter's. Rome 1835.
106 *Heinrich Bürkel*. Street Scene in front of an Italian
    Osteria. 1831.
107 — The Bear-Tamer's Visit to an Italian Village. 1831.
114 *A. F. Elsasser*. View from the antique Theatre in
    Taormina.
116 *Philip Foltz*. Italian Beggar Girl, sleeping. 1836.
117 — Composition Sketch from Uhland's Poem, "Des
    Sängers Fluch". 1837.

136A *F. Overbeck.* The Good Shepherd. Loan from the
the Ny Carlsberg Glyptotek, Copenhagen, 1943.

142 *J. C. Reinhart.* From the Roman Campagna. 1823.

152 *J. Riepenhausen.* Venus and Adonis.

158 *G. Schick.* Landscape with biblical figures, Ruth and
Boaz. The landscape in middle distance and background is the work of *J. A. Koch.*

159 *J. H. Schilbach.* Forum Romanum. 1825.

302A *H. Reinhold.* Scene from the Isle of Capri. Unfinished.

ROOM LIII

4 STATUETTE. *Pietro Galli.* The invention of the Syrinx.
Pan with the Flute, and Cupid. Marble.

PAINTINGS

82A *Vincenzo Giovannini.* A Chemist in his Laboratory.

85 *F. Storelli.* Italian Landscape. 1833.

90 *Th. Gudin.* Shore at Naples. 1837.

97 *G. Lazzarini.* Copy after *F. M. Granet:* The Choir in
the Capuchin Monastery, near the Piazza Barberini,
Rome.

118 *C. W. von Heideck.* From the Defence of a Spanish
Town during a Guerilla War. 1841.

153 *J. Riepenhausen.* Cupid instructing two young Girls.

154 — Bramante presenting Raphael to Pope Julius II.

155 — Roman Second-Hand Bookseller.

167 *M. Wittmer.* Aesop, seated on a Stone Seat over a
Fountain, telling Fables to the People. 1841.

169 *Karl Markó.* Lake Nemi. 1834.

252 *J. L. Lund.* Italian Landscape.

ROOM LIV

RELIEFS. On the window wall. *H. E. Freund:* Selene, the Goddess of the Moon, and Helios, the God of the Sun. Models (plaster) for the capitals of the pilasters on the main front of the Museum, executed in sandstone by *Johan Scholl* in 1843.

PAINTINGS

7   *Italian Artist* from the 16th century. Mary surrounded by her Relations.

8   *Italian Artist* from the 16th century. Male portrait.

9   *Italian Artist* from the end of the 16th century. Young Lady.

12   *Italian Artist* from the end of the 16th century. Rest on the Flight to Egypt.

14   *Italian Artist* from the 16th century. Mary and Child.

15   *School of the Carraccis.* Venus and Cupid.

25   *Artist influenced by El Greco.* Whitsuntide Festival.

31   *Italian Artist* from the 17th century. Landscape.

32   *Italian Artist* from the 17th century. Landscape.

33   *A. Locatelli.* Landscape.

44A   *P. Brill.* Mountainous District.

45   *In the Manner of Pieter Brueghel the Younger.* The Temptations of St. Anthony.

47   *Dutch Artist* from the 17th century. A Man with a Wine Glass.

48   *Lieve Verschuir.* Seascape.

49   *J. F. van Bloemen.* Landscape.

51   *In the Manner of A. F. Boudewyns and Peeter Bout.* A Ferry.

52   — Road along a River.

53   — Street Scene.

56 *Hendrik Voogd.* Italian Landscape.
306 The Ecstasy of St. Francis. Miniature, a Copy after
     an old Italian painting.

ROOM LV

On the window wall: The *Sonne Frieze* on the street frontage of the Museum, in a lithographic reproduction executed by *F. C. Lund,* and coloured by the painter, *Mimi
Bille, c.* 1891-92. Continued in Room LVI.

COPIES AFTER OLDER PAINTINGS

34 Madonna and Child. *C. D. Blunck* after *Perugino.*
35 "Madonna del Granduca". *D. C. Blunck* after *Raphael.*
37 "The Violin Player". *C. Eggers* after *Sebastiano del
     Piombo.*
40 The Education of Cupid. Old Copy after *Tizian.*
54 Male Portrait. *D. C. Blunck* after *B. van der Helst.*

ROOM LVI

On the window wall: The *Sonne Frieze* on the street frontage of the Museum. Lithographic reproduction by *F. C.
Lund;* coloured by the painter, *Mimi Bille, c.* 1891-92. Continued from Room LV.

DRAWINGS AND WATER-COLOURS

2 *Antonio Aquaroni.* The Titus Arch in Rome. 1825.
    Pencil and sepia.
3 — From the Colonnade, St. Peter's Square. Pencil
    and sepia.

6   *Thorvaldsen*. Self-portrait. Rome 8th September, 1811. Pencil, black and white crayon. Purchased 1865.

12 *F. Diofebi*. Interior from the Lateran Church, Rome. Water-colour.

15 *J. Ferrari*. Pope Leo XII, being carried in procession through the Colonnade, the Piazza of St. Peter's. Pencil and sepia.

161 *L. Dupré*. A Greek Youth. Water-colour.

168 *George Augustus Wallis*. Historical Landscape with Votive Procession. The figures are undoubtedly by *Thorvaldsen*. Pencil and sepia.

172 — Historical Landscape. "Ave Maria". The figures are undoubtedly by *Thorvaldsen*. Sepia and water-colour.

173 *W. Wyld*. Scene from the Harbour of Algiers. 1833. Water-colour.

190 *C. H. Kniep*. View of Naples. 1819. Pencil.

202 *J. A. Koch*. Dante and Virgil, upon the Monster Ge-ryon, are taken to the 8th circle of Hell, Male-bolge. The composition is by *Thorvaldsen*. Water-colour.

263 — Boaz and Ruth. Water-colour.

265 — Landscape from Switzerland. Water-colour.

282 *Rudolf Meyer*. Waterfall, Tivoli. Water-colour.

284 *Wilh. Noack*. Drawing after L. Robert's painting. The Interior of the Church of S. Paolo fuori le mura on the Day after the Fire of 1823. China ink and sepia.

286 *J. C. Reinhart*. Heroic Landscape. 1813. Sepia.

289A — Landscape, showing a Waterfall. Watercolour. Loan from the Ny Carlsberg Glyptotek, Copenhagen, 1943.

297 *J. H. Schilbach*. Landscape from Tyrol. Water-colour.

301 *J. Steingrübel*. View of Peschia. 1834. Water-colour.

303 *C. Werner*. The Council Hall of the Ten Man's Committee in the Palace of the Doges, Venice. 1833. Water-colour.

315 *J. C. Dahl*. Near Civita Castellana. 1817. China ink.

325 A *D. C. Blunck*. Thorvaldsen and his Shipmates on the Journey home from Rome, in 1838, on board the Frigate "Rota". 1838. Pencil. Purchased 1882.

327 *Asmus Jacob Carstens*. The Dance of the Muses on Helicon. Pencil.

330 — The Giants assaulting Olympus. Water-colour.

379 *C. F. F. Stanley*. Project for a Theatre Frontage. Naples, 1803. China ink.

406 *Unidentified Artist*. A Billiard Room. Water-colour.

418 — From the Beach near Carrara; two big marble blocks being hoisted on board a ship up on land. Pencil. China ink and white colour.

420 — Copy of the antique mosaic floor in the Sala rotunda in the Vatican. Water-colour.

ROOM LVII

WORKS BY THORVALDSEN

341 A RELIEF. The Dance of the Muses on Helicon. 1804. Marble (Thorvaldsen). Unfinished.

589 A — Yuletide Joy in Heaven. Nysø 1842. Marble (Thorvaldsen). Unfinished.

503 A Four fragments of the marble copy of the Alexander frieze which were partially saved from the fire of Christiansborg Palace in 1884. Executed in Thorvaldsen's studio, Rome.

No. 325 A. Blunck: Thorvaldsen and his Shipmates during
the journey home with the frigate "Rota".

*1, Thorvaldsen. 2, Captain Dahlerup. 3 and 4, Lieutenant Commanders
Fisker and Liebman. 5, 6 and 7, Lieutenants M. Suenson, Flensborg and
Thulstrup. 8, 9, 10, 11, 12, 13 and 14, Second Lieutenants C. A.
Meyer, C. Wulff, Kinch, A. Wilde, Buchwald, Hedemann and Jacobsen.
15, Blankensteiner, Secretary. 16, Bisserup, Bailiff. 17, Krieger, Chief
Surgeon. 18, Hansen, Second Surgeon. 19, Brincken, Chief Mate. 20,
H. J. Dahlerup, Son of the Captain. 21, J. F. Frøhlich, Musician (leader
of the orchestra, The Theatre Royal, Copenhagen). 22, the painter
Blunck. 23, the sculptor Matthiä.*

In the *showcase* are other fragments of the same frieze. Together with the foregoing, presented by the Ministry of the
Interior in 1919.

PORTRAITS OF THORVALDSEN

BUST. *Wilh. Matthiä.* Thorvaldsen. 1833. Plaster.
— *Unidentified Artist.* Thorvaldsen. Marble. Presented
by B. H. Jacobsen, Esq., London, in 1921.

BUST. *Pietro Bienaimé*. Thorvaldsen. 1826. Plaster. Presented by Mrs. Vincenza Aubert de Rossi, Rome, in 1914.

— *Pietro Tenerani*. Thorvaldsen. A cast of the marble copy of 1824 in the San Luca Academy, Rome. Loan from the Ny Carlsberg Glyptotek, Copenhagen, 1943.

ROOM LVIII

PORTRAITS OF THORVALDSEN AND PERSONAL SOUVENIRS

In the *showcase under the window* are various objects and portraits which are in some way or other connected with Thorvaldsen. Among other objects two portraits, in colour, of Anders Grønlund (Attorney and Bailiff) and his wife, drawn by *Thorvaldsen* about 1795 and a photographic reproduction of the daguerreotype of Thorvaldsen taken by *A.-C.-T. Neubourg* in 1840, one year after the invention of modern photography.

PAINTINGS AND DRAWINGS, ETC.

131A *Dietrich Wilh. Lindau*. Thorvaldsen. Oil painting. *C.* 1825. Purchased 1888.

205 *Em. Bærentzen*. The Actress Johanne Luise Heiberg. Oil painting. 1841.

218A *J. Vilh. Gertner*. Thorvaldsen. Oil painting, *c.* 1839. Presented by the Barony of Holstenshus, 1923.

220B *Constantin Hansen.* Jonas Collin, (Danish) P. C., Chairman of the Committee for Thorvaldsen's Museum. Oil painting. 1851. Presented by a circle of Collin's friends on the occasion of his 50 years anniversary, in 1851.

262A *H. D. C. Martens.* Pope Leo XII visiting Thorvald-
    sen's studios near Piazza Barberini, Rome, on
    Lucas Day, the 18th October 1826. Oil painting
    1830. Loan from the Royal Gallery of Fine Arts,
    Copenhagen, 1920.

282A *Paul Mila.* Thorvaldsen. 1823. Drawing, pencil and
    black crayon. Purchased 1935.

312   *C. W. Balsgaard.* Copy after C. W. Eckerberg's por-
    trait of Thorvaldsen from 1814. Overglaze on
    porcelain.

355A *Troels Lund.* Piazza Barberini with Palazzo Barberini,
    Rome. Water-colour. Purchased 1941.

*

In the *cabinet* on the back wall are clothes and weapons
which belonged to Thorvaldsen. Among other things two
working blouses, caps to wear at home and in the studio,
his uniforms as member of the French academy in Rome
(with green embroidery) and of the San Luca Academy in
Rome (with the black silk cape over the shoulder), both
with matching three-cornered hats and rapiers, his tail-coat
and his tall silk hat (all presents from Captain J. C. Jacobsen,
of the Carlsberg Brewery, 1875). Further, his stick and
street-lantern, a couple of light travelling pistols and his
lottery punch (of brown leather) from Nysø.

*

STATUETTE. *Wilh. Matthiä.* Thorvaldsen. 1838. Pla-
    ster.

— *P. Ricco.* Thorvaldsen. Rome 1834. Burnt clay.
    Loan from the Ny Carlsberg Glyptotek, Copen-
    hagen, 1943.

STATUETTE. Possibly *Søren Seidelin Winther*. Thorvaldsen. Ivory. Bequeathed by Mrs. Stephanie Kehlet, née Møller, 1925.

— *Unidentified Artist*. Thorvaldsen. Bronze. Purchased 1933.

20A BUST. *Chr. D. Rauch*. Thorvaldsen 1816. Plaster. Presented by Mr. Eichler (art plasterer), Berlin, in 1870.

6 PORTRAIT MEDALLION. *Unidentified Artist*. Thorvaldsen. Bronze. From a self-portrait drawn by Thorvaldsen (see No. 6, Room LVI).

7 — *Desiderio Cesari*. Thorvaldsen. 1825. Gilded bronze.

8 — Same Artist. Thorvaldsen. 1835. Gilded bronze.

8A — *Franz Woltreck*. Thorvaldsen. 1836. Bronze. Presented by Consul General, Johan Hansen, 1940.

16B RELIEF. *P. F. Rauner*. Thorvaldsen. 1844. Wax. Purchased 1904.

Jørgen Sonne. Thorvaldsen. C. 1846. Coloured plaster. Preliminary for the frieze on the street frontage of the Museum. Purchased 1938.

ROOM LIX

PORTRAIT PAINTINGS

115 *F. Flor*. Elisa Paulsen, Thorvaldsen's daughter, the wife of Colonel Fritz Paulsen. Oil painting 1838.

121A *Eduard Heuss*. Thorvaldsen. Oil painting. 1834. Loan from the Ny Carlsberg Glyptotek, Copenhagen, 1916.

132 *Eduard Magnus*. Thorvaldsen in his working Apparel. Oil painting, *c.* 1825.

174 A *Apollinarij Horawskij.* Thorvaldsen. Copy, executed
in 1852, after a painting by *Orest Kiprenskij* 1833,
in The Russian Museum, Leningrad. Presented by
Consul General Johan Hansen, 1937.

*

Under the window is a big *Iron Box* (the test piece of Berg,
a Copenhagen master smith), which Thorvaldsen bought,
in 1842, on his return from Italy for the storing of his valu-
ables; he never used it, however (see page 82 of C. F.
Wilckens: "Træk af Thorvaldsens Konstner- og Omgangsliv", Copenhagen 1874).

*

In *the cabinet on the back wall are* a number of *Death Masks*
of well-known and unknown persons, some of which
Thorvaldsen used when executing portrait busts. There are
also a few *Life Masks.* Above, Thorvaldsen's death mask
(with the laurel wreath) and a life mask of Thorvaldsen,
made by Count *Savarelli,* presumably about 1810. Below
are the death masks of Napoleon, King Carl XII of Sweden
(in the light of later investigations the identity of this death
mask must be considered doubtful), the popes Pius VII and
Leo XII, Cardinal Consalvi, General Schwarzenberg, the
Duke of Leuchtenberg, August von Goethe (son of the
Poet), Georg Zoëga, Jacob Baden, M. G. Bindesbøll (received in 1892 from the estate of the sculptor F. G. Hertzog
and presented by his sister Mrs. C. B. Jensen) and Mrs.
Høyer (the painter C. F. Høyer's mother). In the middle of
the cabinet are the life mask of Goethe (executed in 1807
by *Karl Gottlob Weisser*), and a portrait head of Sir Thomas
Maitland, possibly by the Greek sculptor *Paolo Prossalenti.*

ROOM LX

CASTS OF ANTIQUE WORKS

Below the window are fragments of statues (hands, arms, feet etc.) which were presumably used in Thorvaldsen's studio for purposes of study.

Mention may be made of: No. 257, Apollonian votive relief. Apollo with the Lyre, accompanied by his Mother and Sister, before the Goddess of Victory. The original at the Villa Albani.–Nos. 260-65, Jupiter, Juno, Mercury, Minerva, Mars, and Venus. Six reliefs from the bases of the incense altars (thymiateria) which now form the lower part of the Barberini candelabras in the Vatican. These are the works of the so-called Neo-Attic School, a Roman style of art that preferably used ancient Greek models. Found in Hadrian's Villa in the 17th century.–No. 285, a Circus Genius, chariot-racing. Fragment of a relief.–Nos. 292-93, the two sides of a low, four-sided marble altar, presumably the base of a censer (thymiaterion), with winged chimeras in the corners. No. 292, Bacchus' beneficial Visit to Mankind. The bearded Bacchus and his train are entering a human dwelling, where a man and his wife are lying at table; a little satyr is taking off the god's sandals whilst another supports him. No. 293, The Purging of the Soul, represented by two weeping cupids who are burning a butterfly (Psyche) with two torches by an incense altar. On the sides are two centaurs with the attributes of Bacchus; one of them is carrying a young zither-playing satyr on his back, the other is bending his knee and stretching up his hand to a bacchante, sitting on his back, to help her down. Relief from the Villa Negroni in the Vatican.–No. 229, The Giants' War against the Gods. Relief from the front of a Roman sarcophagus in the Vatican.–Nos. 302-303, The

Seasons, personified as reclining female figures and small genii. Relief from the front of a Roman sarcophagus lid in the Vatican; it has been placed over the so-called Hadrian Sarcophagus where it never originally belonged.–No. 307, a Nereid upon a Sea Horse surrounded by Cupids. –No. 346, a Bacchante performing an ecstatic dance, waving a thyrsus. Fragment.–No. 353, Venus visiting Anchises. Relief in the British Museum, London.

On the wall opposite the window are fragments of the relief frieze on the *Trajan Column,* which was erected in the Trajan Forum in Rome, completed in A.D. 113, to commemorate Trajan's conquest of Dacia. Heads of the Danubian River-God, with a wreath of rushes round his head (No. 323); heads of the Emperor Trajan (No. 324), Roman priests and warriors (Nos. 325-28), Dacians (Nos. 330-332 and 335), and Sarmatian horsemen (No. 333) (see also No. 336 in Room LXI and No. 322 in the Storage Gallery).–Finally, fourteen heads of Romans from the Emperor *Titus' Triumphal Arch* and other Roman monuments from the Empire period (Nos 308-21).

ROOM LXI

CASTS OF ANTIQUE WORKS

No. 256, nine heads from The Procession of the Gods on a parapet (puteal) round a well, found outside Porta Flaminia near Rome; now in the Capitoline Museum.–No. 282, relief fragment with two Bacchic masks.–No. 283, fragment with a Medusa head.–No. 284, fragment, Antonius' face. At the Villa Albani.–No. 291, three Greek athletes, as victors. Over two of them are the names of Demetrios and Menestheus. In the Vatican.–Nos. 300-01, Niobe's sons and daughters. Reliefs from the lid of the Niobide sarcophagus in the Vatican.–No. 305, Hercules Silvanus. Relief in the Palazzo Rondanini, Rome.–No. 336, Heads of horses and cattle from the Trajan Column (see Room LX). –No. 339, Head of a Roman from the Antoninean period; formerly considered to be the head of Persius, the satirist. At the Villa Albani.–No. 343, fragment. Spring personified as a young woman.–No. 344, Paris driving away in a Quadriga with Helen.–No. 347, a young Satyr playing with a Ram.–No. 348, Fragment. A Dancing Woman.–No. 351, a Circus Biga passing a Goal Post (meta).–No. 352, The Ilian Panel, showing the Trojan War presumably used for educational purposes. Relief fragment found near Via Appia, Rome; now in the Capitoline Museum.–No. 354, a Greek in Combat with Amazons.

A WORK BY THORVALDSEN

127   *Plaster Sketch for a Statue*. Maximilian I, Elector of Bavaria. Original model.

BUSTS FROM THORVALDSEN'S TIME

J. H. Dannecker. Schiller. 1794. Cast.

Chr. D. Rauch. Goethe. 1820. Cast.

Chr. Fr. Tieck. Goethe. 1801. Cast.

David d'Angers. Goethe. Colossal head. 1821. Cast.

Unidentified Artist. Jean-Jacques Rousseau with a Fur Cap. Cast.

J. J. Busch. Friederike Brun, Danisæ Poetess. Rome 1796. Cast.

Domenico Cardelli. Portrait of a Lady. Original model(?).
    — Countess Sophie Magdalene Knuth, née Moltke. 1796. Cast.

Alexander Trippel. Dorothea Schlözer (?). Cast.

STORAGE GALLERY

This gallery, which has been set aside for purposes of study, contains part of the collections of casts and newer sculptures which it has been found impracticable to include in the main collection. It further comprices some few original works by Thorvaldsen, chiefly of secondary interest, as well as replicas and duplicate casts, etc. Owing to the circumstances the contents of this storage gallery are not placed in any fixed order, but the following items may be emphasized. Where nothing to the contrary is stated, they are of plaster.

WORKS BY THORVALDSEN

83 STATUE. Christ. Preliminary work in half-size for the monumental statue (see No. 82 in the Christ Hall). Probably modelled by *Pietro Tenerani* in 1821 from a design by Thorvaldsen and under his supervision.

94 — The Apostle Judas Thaddeus. This is the first execution of the statue, which was modelled in 1823 in Thorvaldsen's studio by *Pacetti* and altered in 1827. Later rejected by Thorvaldsen and substituted by No. 105 in the Christ Hall.

95 — The Apostle Andrew. The first execution of the statue modelled in 1823 in Thorvaldsen's studio by *Joseph Hermann*. Later rejected by Thorvaldsen and substituted by No. 108 in the Christ Hall.

209 BUST. Portrait of a Man. Colossal Bust. Original model. *C.* 1804-05. Formerly called A. P. Bernstorff.

A 869 — Elisa von der Recke. Half-size. Presumably in the winter of 1805-06. Marble (Thorvaldsen). Purchased 1931.

9

A 703 BUST. Auguste Böhmer. In the shape of a herm.
Marble (Thorvaldsen). Hewn 1811-14 on the basis
of Chr. Fr. Tieck's bust (see No. 28 a, page 153);
intended for the monument for which Thorvaldsen
executed the reliefs No. 614 A, Room XIII.

A 887 — Ghazi 'L-Din Haidar, Padshah of Oudh. 1824.
Marble (Thorvaldsen). Purchased 1949.

519 RELIEF. The Genius of Light. Medallion. Original
model. Nysø 1841. Sketch for a medal to be awarded deserving scientists, scholars and artists. Struck
during the reign of King Christian VIII.

673 — Medallion. Sketch for the reverse of King Christian VIII's Coronation Medal.

EGYPTIAN RELIEFS

Casts from Egyptian obelisks erected in Rome. Nos. 204-22,
from the obelisk on Monte Citorio.–Nos. 223-33, from
the obelisk in the Monte Pincio Gardens.–Nos. 234-52,
from the obelisk on the Piazza di Sta. Trinitá de' Monti.

ROMAN ANTIQUES

No. 44, Hermaphrodite. Reclining statue. The figure is
antique and was found in Diocletian's Therms in Rome.
The mattress is hewn by *Bernini* from another antique. The
original was formerly in the Villa Borghese, but is now in
Louvre, Paris.–No. 54, Fragment of a group.–No. 96, an
Eagle.–No. 101, Jupiter Serapis. Colossal head.–No. 103,
Minerva colossal head. From the so-called Albani Bust,
Munich.–No. 122, Head of the Farnese Hercules. The
statue is in the museum in Naples.–No. 125, Ajax's Head
from the group, Ajax with Patroclus' Body, in the Vati-
can.–No. 126, Mars. Bust in the Louvre, Paris.–No. 163,
Antinous. Colossal bust, found in Hadrian's Villa, now

in the Vatican.–No. 614, Antinous. Colossal bust, in the
Louvre, Paris.–No. 166, Antinous. Head and breast of a
colossal statue, found 1738 in Hadrian's Villa; now in the
Capitoline Museum in Rome.–No. 173, The Emperor
Lucius Verus.–Nos. 186-187, Roman portraits.–No. 193,
Julius Cæsar.–No. 322, Victory recording the Exploits of
the Romans on a Shield. Between two trophies of Dacian
weapons. Reliefs from the Trajan Column (see Room LX).

FROM THE RENAISSANCE

No. 1, the Head of Michelangelo, made in *Daniele da Vol-
terra's* workshop. Probably a cast of the bronze head on
the marble bust in the Capitoline Museum, Rome.–No. 2,
Madonna Taddei. A tondo relief by *Michelangelo* in the
Royal Academy, London.–No. 4, Imaginary Head. Architectural ornament from the 16th century.–No. 5, Sa-
lome dancing before Herodes. Marble relief by *Donatello*
in the museum in Lille.–No. 8, Bowl showing hunting
scenes in arabesques. The original, from the 16th century,
is of metal. – No. 9, Helmet from the 16th century (so-
called borgognotta). On one side is the Judgment of Paris,
and on the other is the Abduction of Helen.–Nos. 12-13,
Heads of children; by *François Duquesnoy*. – Nos. 14-15,
Mask and bust of sleeping child; by *François Duquesnoy* or
his school.–No. 97, Walking bull. Statuette by *Giovanni da
Bologna*. Presumably after a replica from *Francesco Lusini's*
workshop.

18TH AND 19TH CENTURIES

 2 *A. Bezzi.* A little Dice Player. Marble.
21 *Francis Chantrey.* Sir Walter Scott. Colossal bust.
21 A *J. H. Dannecker.* Schiller. Colossal mask.
27 *Giuseppe de Fabris.* Pope Gregory XVI. Bust.

9*

John Flaxman. Henry Philip Hope, Thomas Hope's brother. Bust. Marble. Bought at the Hope sale in England, in 1917.

3   *Pietro Galli*. The little Bacchus. Statue. Marble.

5   — Olympus, the Inventor of Flute Playing. Statue. Marble.

23 a *Herman Schievelbein* (?). Karl Freiherr von und zum Stein. Cast. Presented by Mr. Eichler (art plasterer) in Berlin, 1870.

Johan Tobias Sergel. The painter, N. Abildgaard. 1794. Portraitmedallion.

30   *Filippo Tagliolini* (?). Colossal female head, modelled for the restoring of the antique, so-called Farnesian Flora in the museum in Naples.

28 A *Chr. Fr. Tieck*. Auguste Böhmer. 1804. Bust (See Thorvaldsen's marble bust of the same No. A 703, page 128), which is executed on the basis of the present bust).

Alexander Trippel. The painter, N. Abildgaard, Rome *c.* 1776-77. Bust. Cast. The original is in the Royal Academy of Fine Arts, Copenhagen. Presented by the Royal Academy 1941.

26   *Emil Wolff*. Karl Josias von Bunsen. Bust.

Unidentified Artist. Thorvaldsen. Bust. Loan from the Ny Carlsberg Glyptotek, Copenhagen, 1943. (See the marble copy of this in Room XXXVIII).

9   *Unidentified Artist*. The architect, K. F. Schinkel. Portrait medallion. Zinc.

Unidentified (British?) Artist. Silence. Statue. Marble. Bought at an auction in London 1920.

Unidentified (Polish?) Artist. The Death of Prince Jozef Poniatowski. Relief.

DANISH ARTISTS

H. V. Bissen. Ludvig Bødtcher, Danish Poet. 1826. Bust. Purchased 1926.

19 — Thorvaldsen. 1831. Bust.

32 *Chr. Christensen.* Thorvaldsen, standing, leaning against his statue of "Hope". After Thorvaldsen's self-portrait statue. 1845. Medallion. The model for a medal which was to have been issued on occasion of Thorvaldsen's death.

33-34 — Victory in her Quadriga. Two medallions, marked "D. V. Januar" and "Juli 1845" respectively. Sketches for the above-mentioned medal. The finished medal is the work of H. Conradsen (see examples in the showcase in Room XXXI).

G. Chr. Freund. Cupid and Psyche. Modelled 1887 after a relief which Thorvaldsen is said to have executed in Dresden in 1841. Presented by G. Chr. Freund, 1887.

Andreas Paulsen. The archaeologist, Georg Zoëga. Portrait medallion. Marble. Purchased 1887.

Th. Stein. Thorvaldsen's valet, C. F. Wilckens. 1871. Bust. Marble. Presented by the artist 1877.

* * *

LIST OF THORVALDSEN'S WORKS

STATUES AND MONUMENTS, PLASTER SKETCHES
FOR THE SAME

Achilles and Penthesilea: No. 657 (p. 99).

Adonis: No. 53 (p. 28). No. 53A (p. 48).

Aesculapius: Nos. 20-21 (p. 81).

The *Angel* of Baptism, 1823: No. 110 (p. 28). No. 111 (p. 78).

The Angel of Baptism, c. 1828: No. 112 (p. 35). No. 112A (p. 78).

Angels (for the Pius VII. monument): No. 146 and No. 147 (p. 29).

Kneeling Angel: No. 159 (p.78).

Apollo: No. 3 (p. 55).

The Apostles:

Andrew, 1823: No. 95 (p. 117).

Andrew, altered: No. 108 (p. 34). No. 109 (p.78).

Bartholomew: No. 99 (p. 34). No. 100 (p. 78).

James the Greater: No. 98 (p. 34).

James the Less: No. 91 (p. 34). No. 92 (p. 78).

John: No. 89 (p. 34). No. 90 (p. 78).

Matthew: No. 87 (p.34). No. 88 (p. 78).

Paul: No. 103 (p. 34). No. 104 (p. 78).

Peter: No. 86 (p. 34).

Philip: No. 93 (p. 34).

Simon Zelotes: No. 101 (p. 34). No. 102 (p. 78).

Thaddeus, 1823: No. 94 (p. 127).

Thaddeus, 1828: No. 105 (p. 34). No. 106-07 (p. 78).

Thomas: No. 96 (p. 34). No. 97 (p. 78).

Bacchus and *Ariadne:* No. 654 (p. 99).

Bacchus: No. 2 (p. 55).

Princess *Bariatinsky:* No. 171 (p. 42). No. 172 (p. 56).

Eugène de *Beauharnais,* Duke of Leuchtenberg: No.156 (p.26).

Byron: No. 130 (p. 45). No. 131 (p. 45). No. 132 (p. 55). No. 133 (p. 81).

Queen *Caroline Amalie* as Princess: No. 164 (p. 52).

Christ: No. 82 (p. 34). No. 83 (p. 127). Nos. 84-85 (p. 78).

King *Christian IV:* No. 152 (p. 52).

Conradin, the last of the Hohenstaufen Emperors: No. 150 (p. 51).

Copernicus: No. 113 (p. 25). No. 113A (p. 81).

Mars and *Cupid:* No. 7 (p. 28). No. 6 (p. 40).

Venus and Cupid: No. 13A (p. 78).

The Triumphant Cupid, 1814: No. 22A (p. 47). No. 22 (p. 55).

The Triumphant Cupid, 1823: No. 24 (p. 55). No. 23 (p. 65).

PORTRAITS

BUSTS

The Emperor *Alexander I:* No. 246 (p. 44).

St. Apollinaris: No. 186 (p. 29).

Christian, Duke of *Augustenburg:* No. 203 (p. 43).

Frederik, Prince of Augustenburg: No. 205 (p. 29).

Baden, Jacob: No. 221A (p. 30).

Baillie, Alexander: No. 262 (p. 57).

Bariatinsky, Maria Feodorowna: No. 250 (p. 57).

Barlow, George Hilaro: No. 289 (p. 44).

Bartholin, Caspar: No. 227 (p. 56).

Bentinck, William: No. 261 (p. 63).

Bernstorff, A. P., 1795: No. 661 (p. 99).

The same, 1797: No. 662 (p. 99).

Ida Brun, Countess de *Bombelles:* No. 218A (p. 48). No. 218 (p. 56).

Bonar, Thompson Henry: No. A 893 (p. 43).

Donna Catherina di *Branciforte,* Princess of Butera: No. 276 (p. 30).

Brandt, H. Fr.: No. 241 (p. 44).

Bray, François Gabriel de: No. 300 (p. 57).

Brun, Ida: No. 218A (p. 48). No. 218 (p. 56).

Georg Wilhelm Karl Wilding, Prince of *Butera* and Radali: No. 275 (p. 30).

Donna Catherina di Branciforte, Princess of Butera: No. 276 (p. 30).

Byron: No. 256 (p. 30). No. 257 (p. 44).

Bøhmer, Auguste: No. A 703 (p. 128).

Caldoni, Vittoria: No. 279 (p. 49).

Camuccini, Vincenzo: No. 281 (p. 51). No. 282 (p. 72).

Queen *Caroline* Amalie as Princess: No. 198 (p. 51).

Princess Caroline: No. 193A (p. 49). No. 193 (p. 52).

King *Christian VIII,* as Successor to the Throne: No. 197 (p. 50).

Christian, Duke of Augustenburg: No. 203 (p. 43).

Consalvi, Ercole: No. 271 (p. 30).

Coronini-Cronberg, Michael: No. 301 (p. 70).

Craufurd, Jane: No. 307 (p. 49).

Dahl, J. C.: No. 229 (p. 43).

Danneskiold-Samsøe, Conrad: No. 214 (p. 65).

Danneskiold- Samsøe, Henriette: No. 215 (p. 56).

Danneskiold-Samsøe, Louise: No. 216 (p. 65).

Dietrichstein, Alexandrine von: No. 238 (p. 57).

Divett, Edward: No. 263 (p. 44).

Donner, C. H.: No. 242 (p. 44).

Eckersberg, C. W.: No. 224 (p. 36).

RELIEFS AND SKETCHES FOR THE SAME

Hector's Body: No. 492A (p. 39). No. 492 (p. 60).

Chiron, the Centaur, teaching Achilles to throw the Spear: No. 488 (p. 53). No. 488A (p. 49).

The Sea Goddess Thetis dipping her son Achilles in the Styx: No. 487 (p. 31).

Achilles with the slain Amazon Penthesilea: No. 495 (p. 39). No. 496 (p. 60).

Achilles bandaging the wounds of Patroclus: No. 493 (p. 39). No. 494 (p. 60).

Diana and *Actaeon:* Nos. 460–61 (p. 60).

Adam and Eve with Cain and Abel: No. 551 (p. 32). No. 552 (p. 79).

Adonis: No. 476 (p. 60).

Triumphant Entry of *Alexander* the Great into Babylon: No. 503 (p. 27). Nos. 504–05 (p. 31). Nos. 506–07 (p. 32). No. 508 (p. 60). Nos. 509–13 (p. 61). No. 503A (p. 119).

Thaïs luring Alexander to set Persepolis on fire, 1832: No. 514 (p. 47). No. 515 (p. 61).

Same subject, 1837: No. 516 (p. 32).

Cupid received by *Anacreon*-Winter: No. 414 (p. 38). No. 416 (p. 42). No. 415 (p. 59).

Perseus carrying off *Andromeda* on Pegasus: No. 486 (p. 40).

The Child's Guardian *Angel* (for the Schoolchildren's Poorbox in the church of Our Lady): No. 596 (p. 35).

Angels, singing: No. 585 (p. 37). No. 586 (p. 62).

Angels, playing instruments: No. 587 (p. 37). No. 588 (p. 62).

Angels with Flowers and Garlands: Nos. 590–92 (p. 62).

Angels of the Last Judgment: Nos. 593–95 (p. 32).

The *Annunciation:* No. 569 (p. 35).

Apollo: No. 326 (p. 42).

Apollo amongst the Shepherds: No. 344 (p. 79).

Apollo and Daphne: No. 478 (p. 60).

Art and the light-bringing Genius: No. 517 (p. 36).

Art and the light-bringing Genius "A genio turnen": No. 518A (p. 51). No. 518 (p. 61).

The Protection of the Arts and Sciences: No. 607 (p. 80).

Symbols of the Arts and Sciency wreathed by genii: No. 610 (p. 80).

Atalanta: No. 473 (p. 60).

Cupid and the young Bacchus trampling Grapes under Foot — *Antumn:* No. 412 (p. 38). No. 413 (p. 59).

Bacchante holding up a bunch of Grapes for a little Satyr: No. 354 (p. 42). No. 355 (p. 58).

A Bacchante with a Bird: No. 648 (p. 80).

A Satyr dancing with a Bacchante: Nos. 357-58 (p. 46).

Mercury bringing the Infant *Bacchus* to Ino: No. 346 (p. 65). No. 347 (p. 58). No. 347A (p. 46).

Cupid with Bacchus: No. 409A (p. 38). No. 407 (p. 42). No. 408 (p. 59).

Baptismal font: No. 555 (p. 70).

Briseïs being led away from Achilles, 1803: No. 489 (p. 39). No. 490 (p. 60).

Same subject, 1837: No. 491 (p. 31).

Callisto: No. 472 (p. 60).

The *Child's* Guardian Angel (for the Schoolchildren's Poorbox in the Church of Our Lady): No. 596 (p. 35).

Praying Children: No. 628 (p. 62).

Chione and Daedalion: No. 464 (p. 60).

The Centaur *Chiron* teaching Achilles to throw the Spear: No. 488A (p. 49). No. 488 (p. 53).

The Baptism of *Christ:* No. 557 (p. 52).

Christ's Entry into Jerusalem, 1839-40: No. 559 (p. 35).

Christ's Entry into Jerusalem, 1842: No. 574 (p. 80).

Christ on his way to Calvary: No. 560 (p. 35).

Christ entrusting the Government of the Church to the Apostle Peter: No. 564 (p. 35). No. 565 (p. 61).

Christ and the two Diciples at Emaus, 1818: No. 562 (p. 61).

Same subject, 1839 (for the church at Jungshoved): No. 563 (p. 52).

Christ blessing children: No. 566 (p. 79).

The twelve-year-old Christ teaching in the Temple, 1841: No. 567 (p. 32).

Same subject, 1842: No. 572 (p. 35).

Christ and the Woman of Samaria at the Well: No. 568 (p. 32).

St. John baptizing Christ: No. 573 (p. 35).

Christian Charity: No. 597 (p. 35). No. 598 (p. 76).

Christian Charity, with Faith and Hope: No. 599 (p. 52).

The Royal Arms, from the *Court* Chemists: No. 674 (p. 99).

Cupid, resting: No. 672 (p. 100).

Cupid listening to the song of Erato: No. 343 (p. 46).

Cupid feeding Hygeia's Serpent: No. 371 (p. 37). No. 372 (p. 58).

Hygeia being wreathed by Cupid: No. 373 (p. 64).

Cupid, fettered, with the Graces: No. 375 (p. 37). No. 376 (p. 58).

Cupid holding Sway over the World: Nos. 377-80 (p. 48). Nos. 381-84 (p. 58 f.).

Cupid on Jupiter's Eagle: Nos. 385-86 (p. 59).

The Genii of the Arts and Handicrafts: Nos. 546-47 (p. 79).

Astronomy: No. 544 (p. 61).

Comedy: No. 534 (p. 61).

Dancing: No. 536 (p. 61).

Death: No. 614 (p. 44). No. 614A (p. 46). No. 627 (p. 34). No. 626 (p. 62).

The Genius of Death by a sepulcral Monument: No. 622 (p. 33).

Government (for Maximilian's statue): No. 530 (p. 27).

Horticulture: No. 542 (p. 61).

Justice (for Maximilian's statue): No. 531 (p. 27).

The Genius of Light with Pegasus: No. 327 (p. 36).

The Genius of Light. Medallion: No. 519 (p. 128).

Art and the light-bringing Genius: No. 517 (p. 36).

Art and the light-bringing Genius. 'A genio lumen': No. 518A (p. 51). No. 518 (p. 61).

Medicine: No. 541 (p. 61).

Music: No. 535 (p. 61).

Navigation: No. 539 (p. 61).

New Year: No. 548 (p. 36).

Painting: No. 520 (p. 54).

Peace and Freedom: No. 529 (p. 32).

Poetry: No. 532 (p. 61).

Poetry, 1844: No. 527 (p. 54).

Poetry (for the Byron statue): No. 134 (p. 58).

Poetry (for the Schiller statue): No. 136 (p. 26).

Poetry (for the Schiller statue): No. 526 (p. 32).

Poetry and Harmony: No. 528 (p. 51).

Religon: No. 545 (p. 61).

Sculpture: Nos. 522-23 (p. 54).

Sculpture sitting on the Shoulder of the Statue of Jupiter. Chalk sketch on a slate for a relief: No. 524 (p. 75).

Three Genii. Motto of King Christian IV: Regna firmat pietas: No. 153 (p. 79).

Trade: No. 540 (p. 61).

Tragedy: No. 533 (p. 61).

War: No. 538 (p. 61).

*

The Dancing *Graces:* No. 374 (p. 41).

The Graces listening to the song of Cupid: No. 601 (p. 51). No. 602 (p. 61).

Cupid, fettered, with the Graces: No. 375 (p. 37). No. 376 (p. 58).

The Graces, floating: No. 338 (p. 68).

Mnemosyne with *Harpocrates:* No. 337 (p. 49).

Hebe presenting Ganymede with a Pitcher and a Bowl: No. 351 (p. 46).

Hercules receiving the Wine of Immortality from Hebe: No. 317 (p. 27). No. 321 (p. 39).

Hector with Paris and *Helen,* 1809: No. 499A (p. 40). No. 499 (p. 60).

Hector, in Helen's Chamber, upraids Paris for his Cowardice, 1837: No. 500 (p. 31).

10*

41 (p. 50). Nos. 642-45 (p. 62).

The Genius of *Light* with Pegasus: No. 327 (p. 36).

Art and the light-bringing Genius: "A genio lumen": No. 518A (p. 51). No. 518 (p. 61).

Art and the light-bringing Genius: No. 517 (p. 36).

The genius of Light. Medallion: No. 519 (p. 128).

The Ages of *Love:* No. 426 (p. 37). No. 427 (p. 79).

Luke with his symbols, the Ox: No. 583 (p. 32).

Luke, as the first Christian painter: No. 584 (p. 32).

The clergyman, Hans *Madsen* before Johan Rantzau: No. 603 (p. 32).

Venus, *Mars* and Cupid in Vulcan's Workshop: No. 420 (p. 31). No. 419 (p. 41).

Mary with the Infant Jesus and St. John: No. 556 (p. 61).

Mary's Flight from the Slaughter of the Innocents at Bethlehem: No. 571 (p. 61).

The Genius of Light. Sketch for a *medal* to be awarded deserving scientists, scholars and artists. Struck during the reign of King Christian VIII: No. 519 (p. 128).

Medallion. Sketch for the reverse of King Christian VIII's Coronation Medal: No. 673 (p. 128).

Meleager: No. 474 (p. 60).

Mercury bringing the Infant Bacchus to Ino: No. 346 (p.

65). No. 347 (p. 58). No. 347A (p. 46).

Mercury carrying Psyche to Heaven: No. 432 (p. 73).

Jupiter enthroned between *Minerva* and Nemesis: No. 316 (p. 44).

Minerva giving a Soul to the Man made by Prometheus: No. 319 (p. 27). No. 323 (p. 39).

Minerva protecting Virtue, whilst exposing Vice (for the Maitland -monument): No. 600 (p. 27).

Minerva: No. 325 (p. 42).

Mnemosyne with Harpocrates: No. 337 (p. 49).

THE MUSES

The Dance of the Muses on Helicon, 1804: No. 341A (p. 119).

Same subject, 1816: No. 340 (p. 37). No. 341 (p. 58).

Calliope: No. 336 (p. 49).

Clio: No. 328 (p. 49).

Erato: No. 333 (p. 49).

Euterpe: No. 329 (p. 49).

Melpomene: No. 331 (p. 49).

Polyhymnia: No. 334 (p. 49).

Terpsichore: No. 332 (p. 49).

Thalia: No. 330 (p. 49).

Urania: No. 335 (p. 49).

The Muses of Tragedy and Comedy: No. 342 (p. 51).

*

Narcissus: No. 477 (p. 60).

Nemesis reading the Deeds of

Mankind to Jupiter: No. 320 (p. 27). No. 324 (p. 40).

Jupiter enthroned between Minerva and Nemesis: No. 316 (p. 44).

Nemesis in a Biga, followed by the Genii of Punishment and Reward: No. 364 (p. 47).

The Centaur *Nessus* embracing the reluctant Deianira: No. 480 (p. 48). No. 481 (p. 53).

Night with her Children, Sleep and Death: No. 367 (p. 41). No. 369 (p. 58).

King *Numa* Pompilius in conversation with Egeria: No. 682 (p. 101).

The *Nymphs* of Diana: Nos. 467-71 (p. 60).

Hercules and *Omphale:* No. 677 (p. 101).

Diana and *Orion:* Nos. 462-63 (p. 60).

Pan teaching a little Satyr to blow a reed-pipe: No. 352 (p. 42). No. 353 (p. 58).

Pan with the Syrinx, the Pan pipe: No. 479 (p. 60).

A lustful Pan and a Hunting Nymph: No. 356 (p. 58). No. 356A (p. 58).

Hector with *Paris* and Helen, 1809: No. 499A (p. 40). No. 499 (p. 60).

Hector, in Helen's Chamber, upraids Paris for his Cowardice, 1837: No. 500 (p. 31).

Achilles bandaging the wounds of *Patroclus:* No. 493 (p. 39). No. 494 (p. 60).

The Genius of *Peace* and Freedom: No. 529 (p. 32).

Achilles with the slain Amazon *Penthesilea:* No. 495 (p. 39). No. 496 (p. 60).

Perseus carrying off Andromeda on Pegasus: No. 486 (p. 40).

The Apostles *Peter* and John healing the lame Beggar outside the Temple Gate: No. 678 (p. 101).

Christ entrusting the Government of the Church to the Apostle Peter: No. 564 (p. 35). No. 565 (p. 61).

The Apotheosis of the *Poet* (for the Schiller-monument): No. 135 (p. 26).

Achilles and *Priam:* No. 676 (p. 100).

Priam supplicating Achilles for Hector's Body: No. 492A (p. 39). No. 492 (p. 60).

Procession to Parnassus: No. 339 (p. 58).

The Etablishment of *Provincial* Advisory Assemblies in Denmark: No. 605 (p. 79).

Cupid leaving the Couch of the sleeping *Psyche:* No. 428 (p. 37).

Psyche, with her Lamp, approaching the sleeping Cupid No. 429 (p. 37).

Cupid reviving the fainting Psyche: No. 430 (p. 37). No. 431 (p. 59).

Mercury carrying Psyche to Heaven: No. 432 (p. 73).

Cupid and Psyche (series of reliefs): Nos. 433-48 (p. 59).

Cupid and Psyche, "Farewell to Nysø": No. 449 (p. 80).

Cupid and Psyche: No. 450 (p. 53).

The clergyman, Hans Madsen before Johan *Rantzau:* No. 603 (p. 32).

Rebecca and Eliezer at the Well: No. 553 (p. 43).

Three Genii. Motto of King Christian IV: *Regna* firmat pietas: No. 153 (p. 79).

The *Resurrection:* No. 561 (p. 79).

The *Royal* Arms, from the Court Chemists: No. 674 (p. 99).

A *Satyr* dancing with a Bacchante: Nos. 357-58 (p. 46).

Baron *Schubart* bidding Farewell to his dying Wife: No. 618 (p. 33). No. 618A (p. 43).

The Ages of Life and the *Seasons* of the Year: Nos. 638-41 (p. 50). Nos. 642-45 (p. 62).

SEPULCHRAL RELIEFS

Andrea Appiani: No. 601 (p. 51). No. 602 (p. 61).

Vacca Berlinghieri: No. 613 (p. 33).

Philip Bethmann-Hollweg: No. 615 (p. 44).

Countess Borkowska: No. 621 (p. 33).

Auguste Böhmer: No. 614 (p. 44). No. 614A (p. 46).

Baroness Chaudoir: No. 624 (p. 34).

Cardinal Consalvi: No. 612 (p. 33).

Charles Drake Garrard: No. 620 (p. 33).

Lady Lawley: No. 623 (p. 33).

Earl of Newburgh: No. 622 (p. 33).

Princess Helena Poninska's children: No. 616 (p. 33). No. 617 (p. 80).

Count Arthur Potočki: No. 628 (p. 62).

Baroness Schubart: No. 618 (p. 33). No. 618A (p. 43).

Anna Maria Porro Serbelloni: No. 619 (p. 45).

Raffael: No. 611 (p. 32).

Unidentified: A Woman, floating over the Genius of Death, and ascending to Heaven (cf. Chaudoir): No. 625 (p. 34).

*

Shepherdess with a Cupid's Nest: No. 424 (p. 46). No. 425 (p. 75).

Thorvaldsen with the Family *Stampe:* No. 636 (p. 62).

Baron Stampe and his sons, Henrik (the hunter) and Holger (the rider): No. 637 (p. 62).

Cupid with a Swan and Boys Plucking Fruit-*Summer:* No. 410 (p. 38). No. 411 (p. 59).

The Institution of the Last *Supper:* No. 558 (p. 52).

Thaïs luring Alexander to set Persepolis on fire, 1832: No. 514 (p. 47). No. 515 (p. 61).

Same subject, 1837: No. 516 (p. 32).

The Sea Goddess *Thetis* dipping her son Achilles in the Styx: No. 487 (p. 31).

Thorvaldsen with the Family Stampe: No. 636 (p. 62).

Tobias healing his blind Father: No. 613 (p. 33).

The Muses of *Tragedy* and Comedy: No. 342 (p. 51).

Ulysses receiving Achilles' Weapons: No. 497 (p. 41). No. 498 (p. 60).

Venus born of the Foam: No. 348 (p. 38).

Cupid complaining to Venus of a Beesting: No. 417 (p. 46). No. 417A (p. 59).

Same subject, remodelled: No. 418 (p. 41).

Venus, Mars and Cupid in Vulcan's Workshop: No. 419 (p. 41). No. 420 (p. 31).

The Goddess of *Victory* (for the Schiller-monument): No. 137 (p. 26).

Victory, sitting: No. 361 (p. 31). No. 359 (p. 47). No. 360 (p. 58).

Victory, standing: No. 363 (p. 31). No. 362 (p.47).

The Abolition of *Villeinage* in Denmark: No. 604 (p. 79). No. 608 (p. 80).

Cupid received by Anakreon -*Winter:* No. 414 (p. 38). No. 416 (p. 42). No. 415 (p. 59).

Venus, Mars and Cupid in *Vulcan's* Workshop: No. 420 (p. 31). No. 419 (p. 41).

Yuletide Joy in Heaven: No. 589 (p. 32). No. 589A (p. 119).

*   *   *

LIST OF PORTRAITS BY OTHER ARTISTS
AND DEATH AND LIFE MASKS

*　　*　　*

LIST OF THE ARTISTS

whose work is to be found in the Collections of the Museum.
(The figures refer to the pages of the present catalogue)

LIST OF THE ARTISTS

who have participated in the decoration of the Museum building.

(The figures refer to the pages of the present catalogue)

It deserves mentions, too, that the painters *Aug. Barlach* and *F. C. Lund* and the sculptor *Jacob Hallager* have participated in the execution of Sonne's Frieze on the street frontage of the Museum; the painters *F. C. Lund* and *Chr. S. Købke* in the ceiling decorations in Room XLI, *William Klein* and *J. J. G. Guntzelnick* in the ceiling decoration in Room XLII.

In the years 1936-40 the decorations in the courtyard of the Museum were renovated by the painter *Axel Johansen* and after his death by the painter *Axel Salto* under the supervision of the architect *Kaare Klint*.

In april 1951 a complete restoration of the street frontages of the Museum began under the direction of *F. C. Lund*, Chief Architect of the Municipality, assisted by the architect *Johan Pedersen*. As part of the restoration the Frieze by Sonne is being renovated by *Axel Salto*, the painter. The original Frieze is pulled off the walls and mounted on canvas by the painter, Professor *Elof Risebye*.

* * *

The vignettes are reproduced in line work after sketches by Thorvaldsen.

They include the following:

On the title page: Psyche kneeling before the Altar. Pencil and sepia. Sketch for relief for the Palazzo Torlonia.

Page 6: Adonis. Pencil and sepia. Sketch for a relief not executed.

Page 132: Sibyl. Sepia. Sketch for a statue not executed (cf. modelled sketch No. 57 in Room XXXIII).

Page 154: Preliminary sketch for a relief. Sepia. Possibly: Zephyr, with Psyche, floating down from the mountain top where the Oracle had given directions to take her so that she might be seized by a Monster (cf. relief for the Palazzo Torlonia, No. 436 in the Corridor, 1st Floor); or: Psyche being led up to Heaven by Mercury (cf. No. 432, Room XXXI).

* * *

CONTENTS

Registers.

Floor Plans.

*   *   *

No. 162 A. Thorvaldsen leaning on his statue of "Hope". (Room xx).

Thorvaldsen's Museum, built by M. G. Bindesbøll, 1839-48.

Jørgen Sonne's Frieze, executed 1846-50. Facing Christiansborg Palace.

Entrance Gallery, with statues of Copernicus (L) and Poniatowski (R).

The Courtyard of the Museum, with Thorvaldsen's ivy-clad grave.

The Christ Hall, with models for the statues in the Church of
Our Lady, Copenhagen.

Room xxxii. Furniture from Thorvaldsen's apartment in
Charlottenborg Palace.

View of the Corridor on the first floor. Models for statues and busts.

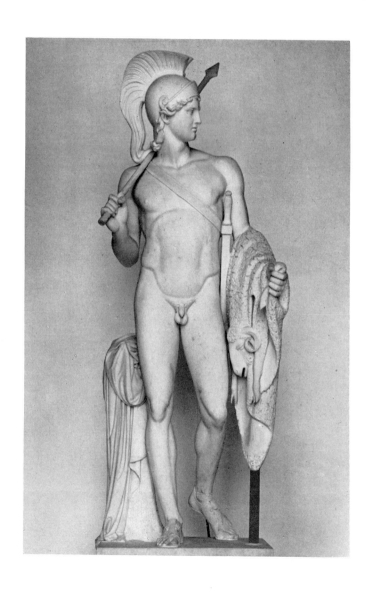

No. 51. Jason. Marble. (Room v).

No. 11. Venus. Marble. (Room IV).

No. 27. Cupid and Psyche. Marble. (Room II).

No. 40. Ganymede. Marble. (Room 1).

No. 4. Mercury. Marble. (Room x).

No. 149. Pope Pius VII. Sketch. (Room XXXIV).

No. 44. Ganymede with Jupiter's Eagle. Marble. (Room XIV).

No. 30. The Graces. Sketch. (Room xxxiv).

No. 657. Achilles and Penthesilea. Sketch. (Room XLIII).

No. 369. Night. Original model. (Corridor, first floor).

No. 492 A. Priam supplicating Achilles for Hector's Body. Marble. (Room v).

No. 370. Day. Original model. (Corridor, first floor).

No. 501 A. Hector saying Farewell to Andromache. Marble. (Room VII).

No. 508. Section of the Alexander Procession. Marble. (Corridor, first floor).

No. 414. Cupid with Anacreon. Marble. (Room IV).

No. 508. Section of the Alexander Procession. Marble. (Corridor, first floor).

No. 518 A. A genio lumen. Marble. (Room xx).

No. 450. Cupid and Psyche. Original model. (Staircase).

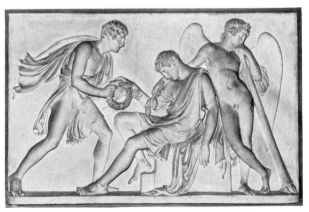

No. 615. Bethmann-Hollweg's Sepulchral Monument. Original model.
(Room XII).

No. 452. Cupid and Hymen. Original model. (Staircase).

No. 553. Rebecca and Eliezer at the Well. Original model. (Room XI).

No. 218 A. Ida Brun. Marble. (Room XVII).

No. 234. Prince Clemens Metternich. Marble. (Room XII).

No. 278 A. Marchesa Florenzi. Marble. (Room XIII).

No. 257. Lord Byron. Original model. (Room XII).

No. 125. J. A. Koch: Apollo among the Shepherds of Thessaly. (Room XXIV).

No. 157. G. Schick: Heroic Landscape. (Room XXIV).

No. 113. P. Cornelius: The Burial of Christ. (Room xxv).

No. 143. J. C. Reinhart: Italian Landscape. (Room xxv).

No. 220. Constantin Hansen: The Poseidon Temple near Paestum (Room XXVI).

No. 238. Jens Juel: View of Little Belt. (Room XXVII).

No. 209. C. W. Eckersberg: Alcyone's Nurse. (Room XXVI).

No. 253. J. Th. Lundbye: Landscape near Arresø. (Room XXVI).

No. 242. J. A. Krafft: Carnival Merrymakers in Rome. (Room XXVII).

No. 78. L. Fioroni: Festival Evening in a Roman Osteria. (Room XXIII).

No. 266. Ernst Meyer: A Public Letter-Writer. (Room xxviii).

No. 199. Blunck: Danish Artists in the La Genzola Osteria. (Room xxxi).

No. 227 A. C. A. Jensen: Baroness Stampe. (Room XXXII).

No. 184. J. C. Dahl: Norwegian Mountain Landscape. (Room XXII).